THE MOUTH
OF THE WOLF

George Paterson about 1945

THE MOUTH
OF THE WOLF

by
JOHN WINDSOR
of Brentwood Bay
British Columbia

GRAY'S PUBLISHING LTD.
Sidney, British Columbia, Canada

INTRODUCTION

by

Field-Marshal The Viscount Montgomery of Alamein, K.G.

I HAVE read this book with the greatest interest. It is a tale of human endeavour in war by brave men who refused to give in—whatever difficulties came their way. It shows what can be done by men of a fighting race who are determined to persevere, and finally to conquer—or die in the attempt.

The author is totally blind. He was serving with the 2nd Canadian Armoured Regiment in Italy, when his tank was hit and he was blinded. He came to England in 1944 for training at St. Dunstan's: he had to learn to be blind, and this he did.

Apart from the purely personal story, the military and soldierly aspects of the book will appeal to many—as, indeed, they did to me. I commend the book to all who are interested in the human side to warfare, which is so often neglected by historians. And the story told by John Windsor has the great merit of being true.

Montgomery of Alamein
F.M.

AUTHOR'S NOTE

THIS is a true story. There may be, because it happened more than twenty years ago, some minor errors and omissions. The names in some cases have been changed to avoid embarrassment and, of course, the conversations have had to be reconstructed. Apart from this, though, every attempt has been made by both George Paterson and myself to tell the story exactly as it happened.

I would dedicate it to all those who worked and fought so that Italy might be free.

JOHN WINDSOR

CHAPTER ONE

T H E engines throbbed and thundered and their roar filled the Whitley's fuselage with a sound that beat down all attempts at conversation. In the shadowy half-light the men lay sprawled about the floor, some asleep, others awake but motionless, each deep in his own thoughts.

George Paterson was one of these. Earlier he had fallen into a fitful sleep, but the flak, as they sped across Sicily, and the Whitley's evasive action had awakened him and now he lay half-propped against the fuselage wall, wishing he could light a cigarette. He glanced at his watch. Twenty-five minutes more, if they were on schedule. He wondered what it would be like.

Only four days ago they had been in England, shivering in fog and ice-cold winter rain while wave upon wave of enemy bombers nightly droned overhead, trying to batter the island into submission.

Tag Pritchard, who was to command the party, had called them together. 'This is an experiment to see what we can do,' he told them. 'We're either pioneers or guinea pigs, however you choose to look at it. The plan, in brief, is for us to jump right into the middle of Mussolini's Italy. We're to blow up a big aqueduct supplying water to the major cities in the South, and then work our way out. Our only hope of getting out is in small parties. We'll have sixty miles of mountainous country to cover to the coast, where a submarine will take us off. Quite simple and straightforward,' he added dryly.

Quite simple and straightforward ... Paterson grinned. He liked Tag, who was brusque and a little puritanical, but with a sense of humour and plenty of guts.

9

Paterson wondered how the men in the other four planes were faring. They were probably experiencing that tight feeling in the pit of the stomach that always comes before a jump. One knew the chances were a hundred to one against anything going wrong, but there was always that one remaining chance that the chute would not come out, or come out but not open. They called it a Roman Candle, and there had been several during the months of training.

His earphones crackled into life and Norman's voice came over the intercom. He was the squadron-leader sent out by the Air Force as an observer.

'George,' he said, 'it's twenty minutes to jump time. Better rouse the men.'

Sitting up, he reached over and shook Jack Watson, his corporal, a phlegmatic north-country man, who nodded and immediately began to shake the sleepers into action. The compartment came to life as the men struggled into their equipment and clipped static lines to the anchor bar. Their faces had a strained look, and George knew they were wondering what it would be like, if it would be as tough as the Commando training in Scotland, if they would jump into a hail of machine-gun fire and die uselessly? Expendable material. He grinned in wry amusement. Like himself, they were probably asking themselves why they had been such damn fools as to volunteer. He glanced round. What had seemed confusion was ordered and purposeful. They were almost ready. Watson was down in the pit, unbolting the jump hatch. Fastening his web belt, he edged along the compartment to plug in the five-pronged check light. It would show that the equipment in the rear bomb bay, the tommy- and bren-guns, the ammo and their share of explosives, was ready to drop when they reached the target area. No light came on.

'Damn,' he swore, inserting it again, and yet again. Still no light.

'The light doesn't come on,' Paterson reported to Norman over the intercom.

'Have you plugged it in the right way?'

'Sir,' snapped back Paterson, 'there is only one possible way to insert a five-prong plug.'

'Well, press the button when you go out. It may be only the light that's gone.'

Moving back to the hatch where the men were now lined up fore and aft in their jump positions, he saw that Watson had the cover almost unbolted. A good N.C.O. and a good paratrooper, almost without nerves.

George glanced at his watch. Seven minutes to go. They could open up now and see what they were flying over. Rough country, if the aerial photos were correct.

As the cover came off and the cold night air filled the compartment, he pulled himself up to his full six-foot-three and breathed in deeply. The troops called him the 'big' Canadian to distinguish him from small, stocky Geoff Jowett from Montreal. Tough and bloodthirsty, Geoff was in one of the other planes, no doubt waiting impatiently to start fighting somebody.

Gripping a stanchion, George peered down through the opening. A full moon etched the world in black and silver. Below them was the lower slope of a mountain, while beyond lay a valley crazy-quilted with ploughland

The red light flashed on. Five minutes to go. Ten years from now, he thought with a touch of amusement, we'll get a few lines in some military history—to the effect that on the night of February 10th, 1941, a party of thirty-six paratroopers of No. 11 Special Air Service Battalion, commanded by Major T. A. G. Pritchard, landed in Italy to blow up enemy installations ... He wondered how the story would go on.

Two minutes to go. He clipped his static line to the bar. Must get the men out fast so they would land close together. Numbers one and two were in position on either side of the hatch, waiting for the signal. When that came, number one would push himself off and drop neatly through the hatch. If he miscalculated, he could smash his face against the edge of the hatch as he went by, and go down with a broken nose or minus a few teeth.

One minute to go. Silently he began to count. 'One Mississippi ... two Mississippi ... three Mississippi...'

Only a few hundred feet below, houses were visible. That should be the village of Calitri. He watched it for a few seconds, greyish white in the moonlight, the black shadows of the walls showing in contrast. Then it was gone, and once again there was ploughland cut by a winding road that hugged the mountain slope.

Twenty seconds. Ten. The moments and the countryside beneath both rushed by and he felt sweat trickle down his side.

Why the hell hadn't the green light come on?

Suddenly, so suddenly as to be startling, it flashed bright. The time for action was now.

With a wave of his hand he sent Peters plummeting through the trap to disappear into the blackness. Then came Tomlinson and Spears, both moving fast ... Half of them out. Now for the equipment. He pushed the button. Nothing happened.

'God damn and blast.' Two more pushes. Still nothing. Can't wait any longer, or they'll be miles out of the landing zone. A wave, and Warner was out. Then Corporal Watson with a slight nod of farewell was gone, leaving George alone. One last try to release the equipment. He pushed the button. Nothing happened. Suddenly the engine noise rose to a crescendo as the pilot jammed the throttle wide open to clear the onrushing line of rock bluffs. Must go now, or not at all.

Sliding his feet over the edge, he pushed, and felt his body dropping. From the half-light of the compartment he plunged into a darkness stabbed by flames from the Whitley's exhausts. As the aircraft, with its roaring engines, receded into the night, he felt his chute open and take hold.

His was jump number thirteen—or 'twelve A', as he preferred to call it. The ground was coming up fast—a ploughed field—and he glanced about to get his bearings. Below and to the right he could see several chutes shimmering pearl-grey in the moonlight, while to the left, partway up the mountainside, the aqueduct stood out bold and clear on its high piers as it stretched across the blackness of a deep ravine.

Then he was down, landing easily on soft mud, so easily that he didn't bother to roll but stood and let the mass of silk collapse about him. Freeing himself, he listened for sounds of fighting, the crack of a rifle or the sharp rattle of a machine-gun. But the only noise to break the stillness was the barking of a dog from a dark mass of farm buildings a little way away.

We've caught the I-ties flat-footed, he thought, as he strode across the field to rejoin his men. They collected in a knot about him, with Watson counting and identifying each new arrival.

'All present, sir,' he reported.

'Okay, Corporal, we'll get up to the aqueduct.'

Fifteen minutes' brisk climbing brought them up the ravine to the foot of one of the massive piers where Tag Pritchard, Flight-Lieutenant Lucky—one of their interpreters—and half a dozen formidable-looking paratroopers were already assembled.

'Is that you, George?' the Major greeted him. 'Jerry

Daly's plane didn't get away from Malta. Developed engine trouble, so you'll have to handle the demolition alone. Jowett, Lee and Deane-Drummond, with their covering parties, are all down and are out looking for the explosive containers and,' he added, 'any Carabinieri that appear on the scene.'

George nodded, mentally appraising the situation. They would be short both Daly's and his share of the explosives, as well as any containers that could not be found in time, but he reckoned to be able to count on six or seven hundred pounds of guncotton.

'I'll take a look at the pier,' he told Pritchard.

Examination produced an unwelcome surprise. The concrete was heavily reinforced with steel, making it much more difficult to demolish. The original plan had been to blow two piers and the abutment, but with only half the guncotton available and the unexpected reinforcing, this might be impossible.

'We might only damage the piers,' he reported to Tag. 'Our best plan would be to concentrate everything on one of them. That would bring the aqueduct down and probably pull the adjoining piers along with it.'

Tag nodded agreement. 'Right, George. Handle it as you think best.'

There was a sharp challenge from down the ravine, an indistinct reply ... laughter ... and then a moment later a party of paratroopers toiled up the slope.

'We've brought in some prisoners,' laughed Deane-Drummond when he joined them. 'We're using them to carry the guncotton. Those forty-pound containers are damned heavy. I don't know what Pichi said, but he certainly put the fear of God into them.' Sergeant Pichi was another of their interpreters, Italian born but a British subject and an implacable enemy of the Fascists.

'We picked up the village station-master on his way to

work,' continued Deane-Drummond. 'The fellow was most upset. Figured he'd be sacked for being late on duty and that they would put him in the army as punishment.' Tony chuckled. 'I promised him a note to give to his superior and now he's quite happy—thinks he'll get a medal for his conduct.'

Under Paterson's directions the containers were laid against the selected pier. In the next hour and a half, as Jowett's and Lee's men brought in additional explosives plus a motley collection of prisoners, peasants and badly frightened Carabinieri police, the preparations advanced quickly. There was still no sign of a general alarm or any attack. In fact, the countryside seemed asleep except for the dogs which barked from scattered houses and from the distant village.

With the guncotton finally in position George fumbled inside his shirt for the detonators, wrapped in cotton-wool, strapped to his chest. With considerable relief he pulled them out and began inserting them. This done, he connected the long length of fuse and reported to Pritchard.

'All ready, sir.'

The Major nodded and glanced about. The covering parties were now in, their job done.

'Chris,' he said to Captain Lee, 'get everybody back about two hundred yards. We're ready to let her go.'

With Pritchard by his side, Paterson lighted the fuse. 'We've got sixty seconds,' he said as they scrambled back to cover. The pair crouched behind an outcropping of rock and waited. The seconds went by at slow march.

'Wish we'd thought to count,' Tag said regretfully.

Still they waited. Nothing happened. George felt sick in his stomach. The others had done their job. Had he failed? What could have gone wrong? Mentally he ran over every step, but could detect no error.

'I'd better go back...' he began, when suddenly the silence was submerged under a great booming roar.

'Thank God,' he breathed, pressing hard against the rock wall as debris crashed down.

After a moment they came from cover to view the chaos. One pier was completely gone. Another leaned at a drunken angle. The aqueduct was cut and dangled crazily as a leaping torrent of water gushed down the ravine and out into the valley beyond.

'A very neat bit of work, George,' commented the older man as they stood together.

'What happened?' called Jowett.

'Listen,' said Pritchard. The sound of the racing torrent, like a mountain waterfall, was sufficient answer. They cheered.

'All right,' continued the Major, 'tie the prisoners and leave them in this hut. We'll divide into three parties. Jowett and Lucky will take one, Lee and Paterson another, Tony and myself the third. We've got five nights to reach the mouth of the Sele River, sixty miles away. The submarine should be waiting to take us off when we signal. You'll have to stay hidden by day and keep off the roads. Once the alarm spreads, all hell will break loose. Remember now, smash the brens and anything else too heavy to carry. We don't want to give the I-ties any presents. Good luck to you all.'

CHAPTER TWO

'WE'RE ready, Chris,' called George, once the surplus equipment had been destroyed. They were old friends, who had been captains together until George had gone on a terrific party before Christmas and got knocked down to second lieutenant for disorderly conduct.

Marching on a compass bearing, they and their troop struck up the mountain slope over rough, rock-strewn land. It was hard going. When they descended to lower levels, they ran into ploughed fields, and here the going was even worse. The mud was gumbo in which they sank to their ankles, and their spirits fell and their tempers sharpened. Thirst plagued them, but they dared not drink the water in their water-bottles. They would need this while they hid during the long daylight hours. At every stream they gulped down draughts of ice-cold mountain water.

As the false dawn lightened the sky, they looked about for a refuge and found it in a shallow, tree-clogged ravine.

They all dropped exhausted on the cold, wet ground and George pulled a map from his battledress pocket. 'Let's see if we can place our position.'

Both he and Chris Lee studied it with increasing gloom. 'I would say we marched at least sixteen or seventeen miles,' estimated Lee, 'yet as the crow flies we've only covered six. Somehow we're going to have to do better tonight.'

They brewed tea over small portable stoves and tried to eat the pemmican they carried. But the stuff was too greasy for their stomachs and refused to stay down.

'It's bloody awful, that's what it is,' commented one of the troopers, trying to satisfy his hunger on a fistful of raisins and a few chocolate squares.

They slept for a while—the heavy sleep of exhaustion—but after several hours the cold soaked up their body warmth and aroused them.

Paterson stirred, became aware of distant voices and snapped awake. Climbing quietly to the lip of the ravine, he peered over. Less than fifty yards away a herd of goats tended by two young boys were grazing.

Sliding back, he whispered to the waking men to keep silent and under cover. It was as well that he did, for presently a spotting plane appeared overhead, flying lazily back and forth, obviously looking for them.

The daylight hours dragged by. Cold and uncomfortable, with conversation no more than a whispered word or two, the only break in the monotony was the sweep past of the searching aircraft, the distant sound of a truck's engine down in the valley and the closer noises of the goatherds. Finally, in late afternoon, the lads drove their animals to a nearby farm. As dusk began to soften the harsh landscape, they emerged, tried to slap some warmth into their chilled bodies and brewed hot tea.

Then came another night of tortuous climbing, slipping, falling, squelching, and at dawn, a vegetation-covered cleft in the rocks high on a mountain slope. They had no herd of goats as neighbours this time and the searching planes were less frequent, but otherwise their condition was as uncomfortable as the day before. At dusk, as they munched their small rations of chocolate and raisins, for none could keep the pemmican down, Lee spoke in a worried tone to Paterson.

'Things don't look too good, George. We've marched hard for two nights and I estimate that we're only seven-

teen or eighteen miles on our way, and we're all weakening
for lack of food.'

The Canadian nodded. 'I think we'll have to take to the
roads and chance it. If we're stopped, we can try to bluff
our way through as a German patrol.'

That night, when the countryside began to quieten and
the lights in the cottages went out, they came down from
the high ground through the morass of ploughed land to a
small road that headed down the valley and began to
march in earnest. The rhythm of their steps and the re-
assuring feel of a solid smooth surface beneath their feet
helped to ease the tiredness and raise their spirits. In an
hour they had covered a good three miles and met not a
soul. A second hour, and another three miles towards freedom.

After a rest, they carried on past a crossroads and along a
stretch where a stream ran beside the road. They came to a
bridge, an ancient stone structure, and were half-way
across with their forward man just reaching the other side
when pandemonium broke loose. Out of the shadows
ahead and into the moonlight jumped six or eight blue-
coated Carabinieri, their rifles at the ready, and all shouting in high excitement.

The paratroopers jerked to a halt, hands going to pistols
while their one tommy-gunner unslung and cocked his
weapon in an instinctive reaction.

'*Deutsch ... Deutsch*,' called out Lee in what he hoped
was a Teutonic tone while the others, taking the cue,
threw in a variety of guttural Germanic sounds.

This apparently impressed no one, and the leader of the
Carabinieri, a fat little sergeant, seemed to bounce up and
down as he hurled back, '*Inglesi, Inglesi, Inglesi.*'

Then a new complication arose. From around the bend
in the road ahead a motley collection of men, women and
children—at least a hundred of them—some carrying shot-

guns, axes or shovels poured forward to mix with the Carabinieri while the more curious advanced cautiously for a closer look.

'We must have been seen,' whispered Paterson disgustedly. 'They were lying in wait for us.'

Lee nodded. 'I suppose we could shoot our way out, but we haven't got a chance of reaching the coast now, and I can't see any point in needlessly slaughtering these poor devils. Some of the women and children would be bound to get it. I'm afraid they've got us.'

Paterson and the others knew it was true, but they were humiliated and angered at being forced to surrender to such a rabble.

The tommy-gun and their pistols were seized. Emboldened by their lack of weapons, the peasants began to mill around, pushing, shoving, all extremely excited. Finally, the troop was herded down the road and around the corner to a small evil-smelling village, where they were pushed and prodded into a large basement with the police and most of the villagers streaming in after them.

While the spectators jeered and spat, they were searched, but none too efficiently, for George lost neither the six gold coins sewn into his jacket collar, nor the minute silk map hidden in a trouser lining, nor the tiny escape compass that was part of his collar stud. The inspection might have gone on longer, but one burly young paratrooper suddenly doubled his fists and growled at a garlic-smelling policeman, 'Keep back, you bloody little ape, or I'll push your God-damn teeth down your throat.' The words were not understood, but the meaning was and the police thereafter kept back a pace or two, all the time covering them with their rifles.

George slumped wearily on a bench, hands thrust deep in pockets, and gloomily surveyed the faces of the crowd. Stupid, ignorant faces, faces full of hatred that was kept in check by a shadow of fear like those of men who torment a caged tiger yet are fearful lest the beast should escape.

A long wait was finally broken by a new noise, the squeaking of carts outside in the street. The officious little sergeant, flanked by a couple of riflemen, pushed his way back into the cellar, carrying a load of chain handcuffs that clinked together as he walked.

Despite their angry protests, the paratroopers were handcuffed and pushed into the street. Trigger-happy Carabinieri prodded them into mule carts. Once again escorted by both police and villagers, they set off along the road like captives in a Roman triumph.

It was broad daylight when the prisoners, unshaven and filthy, reached a small country town with an impressive municipal building, the basement of which served as a gaol. They were unloaded without ceremony, their handcuffs removed, and at gunpoint they were urged into a large community cell that was already occupied.

'So they got you, too,' came the voice of Tag Pritchard. 'We were nabbed yesterday.'

'A couple of youngsters spotted our hideout and they brought the whole blasted countryside down on us,' added Tony Deane-Drummond bitterly while the two parties of paratroopers intermingled, exchanging questions and experiences.

The hours passed slowly. They longed to shave and wash and thought ravenously of food, but their captors, after searching them once again, left them to their thoughts. Outside in the square they could hear a crowd come to applaud the Italian triumph over the hated invaders.

During the afternoon the tone of the crowd suddenly changed, turned hostile. 'What's up now?' queried someone. The cell door opened and a battered group were hurled in.

'My God, it's Geoff Jowett and his party,' exclaimed Lee.

21

'It's us all right,' said Jowett sourly. 'We killed three or four of the bastards.'

'Soldiers?'

'Yes, and armed civilians before they finally got us. They beat us up for it.'

'They're threatening to shoot us as murderers,' explained Flight-Lieutenant Lucky, the interpreter, an older man.

A few minutes later the cell door swung open again and an officer, backed by Carabinieri, shouted something.

'All the officers are to go with him,' translated Lucky.

Are we going to be shot in retaliation? George wondered, but discarded the idea as unlikely. Surely there would have to be a trial first.

They were hustled down a corridor into a smaller cell, but they had no sooner settled on the wooden bench than the door was once again flung open and a small man, his uniform heavy with silver braid, strutted in. He was a red-faced, grey-haired man with bristling white moustaches. After standing and surveying them for several tense moments, his face seemed to go redder than ever and he let fly with a broadside of angry Italian.

'He says,' explained Lucky, 'that he is a general and that we are supposed to stand when he comes into the room.'

Tag Pritchard pondered this while the rest waited for his decision.

'Yes,' he agreed, 'that's correct. I believe by the rules of war or something that we are supposed to.' With that he rose, followed by the others, and immediately the little General's attitude changed.

'You are heroes,' he told them, 'brave men and heroes. Italian officers admire gallant enemies. Be assured, gentlemen, that you will be treated with honour.'

His audience was somewhat embarrassed by this sudden elevation to the rank of heroes, but Pritchard, like a good

22

officer, seized the opportunity 'My men haven't had food in three days, sir. Could they have a meal?'

'Of course. Of course,' replied the General, turning to bark out orders to an aide.

His admiration for their courage produced a meal of bully beef and bread, but they soon discovered that his attitude was not shared by his subordinates. To them anyone who would parachute into enemy country was obviously crazy, probably a condemned criminal, possibly a murderer who had chosen this way of winning a reprieve.

After an extremely uncomfortable night, sprawled on the wooden benches or the far from clean floor, they were again shackled under protest and herded outside.

'Napoli,' one of the guards answered Lucky's question as to their destination.

They were marched under heavy escort of Carabinieri, along several streets, past groups of angry-looking civilians who shook their fists and spat in their direction.

'We're not going to win any popularity contests in this town,' murmured George.

'It's those men Jowett's boys killed. They'd string us up on lamp-posts if they could.'

The train journey was slow, the country picturesque, and it might not have been unpleasant but for the guards. Each paratrooper was wedged between two, and these men varied the monotony by constant spitting.

George felt his stomach turn every time one of his escorts cleared his throat in preparation, and he finally reached the point where he could stand it no longer.

'For Christ's sake, knock it off,' he roared in his best parade-ground manner, at the same time pointing to an obviously displayed *Non Sputare* sign. The little soldier on his right cowered under this unexpected blast, while the others gripped their rifles nervously. It did have some effect as the rate of spitting sharply declined.

Rain was falling through the darkness, cold and depressing to match their spirits, when they reached Naples. Trucks were waiting to carry them through poorly lighted, malodorous streets so narrow and twisted that at times it seemed as if they must crush the shadowy half-seen pedestrians who scurried into the blackness of a doorway or an alley. At last they came to a massive fortress-like structure surrounded by a high wall broken by a heavily guarded gate through which they drove, to halt in a small courtyard.

'The military prison,' Lucky told them after a few words with one of the drivers.

They were lined up in a babble of shouting and confusion, divided into small groups and marched off.

It's like a medieval dungeon, thought George as he was hustled by a pair of rough-looking warders along a dim stone passageway. They came to a heavy door, solid except for a peep-hole, which one of the warders opened with a rattle of keys.

He was a sullen-looking, squatly built man and as he urged George into the cell, none too gently, he managed a few words in broken English.

'You God-damn son of bitch. You pretty soon be shot.' The door banged shut. The key turned in the lock and the young Canadian was left alone to survey his accommodation: a small cell with a slit high in the wall for a window, and a rough wooden bench covered by a damp and dirty straw-filled palliasse its only furniture.

He slumped down tired, hungry and depressed. Normally, except when his temper was aroused, he was able to look upon the world and upon himself with a certain amusement, taking the ups and downs of life calmly and philosophically. But now he was at a low ebb, and the warder's threat added to his black thoughts.

Would they be shot? There was no justification by the

rules of war, but dictators don't go by rules. Yes, he thought gloomily, they might very well be shot, in reprisal for those dead civilians and as a warning to others.

To be wiped out before he had really begun to live ... To be remembered once a year, on Armistice Day ... He swore in sudden anger at the futility of his position.

Then his anger was gone ... He was wrong to think that he wouldn't be remembered. His mother and father, his brothers and his sister, so far away on a British Columbia fruit farm, would never forget, never cease to grieve. His mood brightened as he thought of the Okanagan valley and Kelowna, on the lakeshore. It was three and a half years since he had left to attend Edinburgh University. If it hadn't been for this damned war he'd still be there, drowsing through lectures, drinking beer in the pub with Alastair and 'Lugs', or maybe out on a date with that cute little blonde typist who had not placed too high a premium on her virtue.

Ah well, he reflected, the war had come, and to be honest, he'd enjoyed soldiering, first as an engineer and then with Special Air Service. It had been tough, but his companions had courage and loyalty, and if he died it would be in good company.

Gradually, the strain and uncertainty, the fatigue of the last few days began to master him and he slept.

It was day when he awoke, for there was a greyish light coming in through the slit, and distantly he could hear the sounds of the prison, shouts of command, heavy footsteps, the jangle of keys and the banging of doors. But his own remained obstinately closed.

Time went by—time to pace up and down the little room for restless hours until finally the warder came, not with breakfast but with a gestured command to follow. He was led to a room where two civilians sat behind a long table.

'Good morning,' said one, a fleshy well-groomed man with an affable manner. 'Please sit down. Will you have a cigarette and a glass of wine?'

Ignoring the wine, George took a cigarette, and waited.

'Now, let me see. Your name is Paterson, George Paterson.'

'That's right.'

'And your rank is?'

'Second lieutenant.'

'Good. Now we're officers of the Questura, the secret police, and it's our job to interview all prisoners. Just a formality. But orders are orders. Are you sure you won't have a glass of this wine? It's rather good. No? All right, now when was it you said you left England?'

'I didn't say.'

'Oh, sorry, I thought I'd asked you. We have to have it for the records.'

'I'm sorry,' replied Paterson stonily, 'but I'm only allowed to give my name, rank and number.'

The other's tone lost some of its affability. 'Now come, Lieutenant, we're not asking you to give away any military secrets, we know you wouldn't. All we need are a few details that we can find out anyway, to satisfy the bureaucrats in Rome.'

His tone became oily. 'Believe me, Lieutenant, I genuinely want to help you, and you are in rather a bad situation. You were caught making war on the civilian population and committing acts of sabotage. In Italy that is punishable by death, but if you co-operate and answer a few simple questions I'll be able to use my influence to save you and your friends.'

The man's fleshy, confident face irritated George, and the fact that he hadn't had any food since yesterday on the train added to this irritation. He cast about for an answer that would express his feelings.

'Balls,' he snarled, and the word came out like a slap on the face.

The other flushed angrily. 'Answer me, I say. When did you leave England?'

'I can't answer that question.'

'Where did you do your training?'

'I can't answer that question.'

The interrogation went on for half an hour, but finally the Questura gave up in disgust, angrily calling in the warder to remove the prisoner.

'You'll regret that you didn't co-operate,' was the final vindictive thrust.

George was led back, not to his old cell but to a larger one, and as he stooped to go through the somewhat low door, he saw with pleasure that it was already occupied by his brother officers.

'Welcome back to the family,' greeted Tag.

'You been through the third degree?' asked Geoff Jowett. He snorted. 'The silly sods thought they were being so subtle with their questions.'

'We've all been grilled,' explained Chris Lee, 'and now we're wondering what's next.'

They didn't have long to wait. Within ten minutes a couple of warders brought them some food and a ration of rough country wine. They were too hungry to enquire what the concoction was. With the warders came a young officer and Lucky, between mouthfuls, translated his message.

'As we came in aeroplanes, we're considered Air Force prisoners. So we're being moved out to the air base until they decide what to do with us. As far as I'm concerned,' he added, 'it's bound to be an improvement over this dump.'

He was right. It was a big improvement. Though still heavily guarded, they were given a fourth-floor wing in the officers' quarters, supplied with excellent meals, permitted to bath every second day which their hosts seemed to feel was somewhat excessive, and allowed to exercise back and forth on the flat roof.

The commanding officer at the aerodrome was a Colonel Montalba, who proved to be a courteous and kindly captor. They were badly in need of such minor necessities as razors, toothbrushes, soap and towels, and he allowed Lucky, with a Carabinieri escort, to go down into Naples to purchase these items, both for themselves and for the men who were still being held at the military prison.

Their Questura friends were not through with them yet. One morning they were called down to a room where a photographer and a finger-print expert waited.

'We are not having our photographs or our finger-prints taken,' stated Pritchard in his brusque manner. 'That is for criminals, not prisoners of war.'

The scene became farcical as the prisoners kept turning away and shielding their faces, while the Questurino photographer frantically dashed about, trying to get pictures. In the middle of the confusion the door burst open and Colonel Montalba stormed in, almost apoplectic with rage.

'Swine! Pigs!' he shrieked. 'What are you doing here? How dare you interfere with prisoners of the Royal Italian Air Force without my permission.'

He seized the photographer's plates, smashed them on the floor, followed this with the finger-print outfit and then, working himself up to new heights of anger, grabbed the camera and hurled it through the open window.

'Get out! Get out!' he screamed at the cowering Questurini who bolted through the door like a pair of frightened rabbits.

'Your pardon, gentlemen,' snorted the enraged Colonel as he slammed out in hot pursuit.

On the following day their numbers were increased by

two. They were finishing lunch when the door opened and a couple of dirty, unkempt-looking men strolled in.

'Well, look who's here!' exclaimed someone. 'It's Jerry Daly. We thought you were enjoying life in Malta.'

Daly, a regular captain, grinned. 'Our plane got off about an hour after you left and we followed you in. Didn't want you chaps to have all the fun. Unfortunately the pilot dropped us in the wrong valley. We heard the aqueduct go up just as we landed, and we've been playing hide and seek with the Italians ever since.'

The other man was Bob Wotherspoon, an R.A.F. Whitley pilot who had trained with them in England. On the night of the attack his plane had gone on a separate mission to bomb diversionary targets further inland.

'What happened to you, Bob?' asked Pritchard.

'The flak got one of my engines so I wirelessed back that we'd make for a place called the Sele River, and hope to be picked up there by seaplane, but of course we didn't make it.'

'The Sele River,' broke in Tag. 'Why, Bob, that's where we were making for.'

'Good heavens, I had no idea that was your escape route. It just happened to be the nearest place on the coast. Did I foul things up for you?'

They grinned. 'No, we didn't get half-way there and maybe it's just as well because once your message went out they would have recalled the submarine.'

'You're the unlucky one,' laughed George, 'getting thrown in with us. We're considered a thorough crowd of murdering bastards by the Italians.'

The ensuing days went by in well-fed boredom. A week passed, then another and still, apparently, their fate was undecided. George spent much of his time gloomily looking out of his window at Vesuvius until he came to hate the sight of the volcano with its thin plume of smoke for ever drifting skyward. After three weeks of this aimless existence a break occurred in the daily monotony.

'We're all wanted at Montalba's office. Maybe they've decided what to do with us.'

The Colonel was all smiles and bows as they filed in. 'Gentlemen,' he began, with Lucky translating, 'I have good news. You are to be transferred to a camp at Sulmona up in the mountains. The scenery is magnificent, the food is excellent and there will be plenty of wine and cigarettes. I know you will be happy there with the other British prisoners and you will be able to play football, and that other game you call cricket.'

'Little Utopia,' whispered Jowett cynically.

Montalba had almost reached the end of his catalogue of the varied delights to be found at Sulmona, but there was a bitter pill beneath the sugar coating, and it grieved him to have to administer it to these enemies whom he liked and admired.

'Alas,' he confessed sadly, 'there is one bad thing about the camp. I deeply regret it, gentlemen, but you will be allowed no women.'

CHAPTER THREE

FOR hours the train had passed through barren and desolate country, snow-covered peaks girdled by pine woods, while at the lower levels small poverty-stricken hamlets clung like leeches to the brown, unproductive fields. Then they had plunged into a long tunnel that stabbed the hillside and came out into a valley, more prosperous-looking than the others with its vineyards and ploughed land. From the window they glimpsed a small town ahead, and its name was called up and down the carriage—Sulmona.

So this is it, thought George, as unpretentious stone houses began to slide past the window, and their engine ground slowly to a halt.

'All prisoners are to line up on the platform,' came the voice of the interpreter. Their escort, thirty-five Carabinieri commanded by a colonel, watched them with wary eyes and restless trigger-fingers as they milled and pushed their way outside. It was dusk with a chill rain falling, but the cold air felt good after the stuffiness of the compartments and the thought of exercise (they had been told it was a five-mile march to the camp) was welcome after the days of confinement.

Once they left the town the road was muddy and pot-holed, nothing unusual to the paratroopers inured to English rain and mud, but most unpleasant for their guards who were splendidly turned out in full-dress uniform. They walked gingerly, trying to protect trousers and shiny boots from the splashes.

'Blimey,' mocked an unshaven Cockney stamping hard in a puddle, 'did I muck up your pretty uniform, General?'

Far ahead through the darkness they could see bright

lights resting on the lower slope of a mountain. 'That must be the camp,' George observed to his neighbour. 'Looks rather gay and inviting.'

Closer inspection showed it to be anything but gay and inviting. A high brick wall surrounded by three fences of barbed wire enclosed a rectangle of ten or twelve acres, subdivided by inner walls into a number of compounds. Each had its own mess hut, kitchen and dormitories locked off from the others. Over all this, but especially around the outside, innumerable spotlights blazed down, outlining the defences in a broad band of white light, while from the guard towers sentinels occasionally flicked on searchlights to probe into dark corners with their shining fingers.

An Italian officer with abnormally large feet, and with eyes so wide apart that he immediately won the nickname of 'Fish Eyes', met them at the gate and led them to the guardroom where, in good English, he made them welcome.

'We do not look upon you as soldiers, but as criminals who have made war on our peaceful civilian population and attempted to destroy the glories of Fascism. You will not be allowed to mix with the other prisoners but will be isolated, so that you cannot spread your evil. The Colonel has placed me in charge of you and I give you warning that the slightest infraction of the rules or disobedience of my orders will be severely punished, while if you try to escape you will be shot.'

'Bollocks,' growled several low voices and Fish Eyes, catching the word, eyed them balefully but took no action except to order the guards to march them off.

Paterson and his fellow officers were separated from their men and led along a series of passageways between high walls. Finally, a door was unbolted and they were led into their new quarters, a one-storey building containing a mess room and kitchen in addition to a number of very small cells with a narrow exercise walk along one side. A wall effectively cut them off from the rest of the camp.

Lord, what a dreary dump, thought George, after they had selected rooms and inspected the premises. I wonder how long Fish Eyes plans to keep us here?

In the days and weeks that followed they were forced, against their natures, to accustom themselves to the dreary monotony of prison-camp life, and this monotony, combined with the close confinement, brought tempers and nerves almost to the breaking point. To avoid friction, which would have delighted their captors, they became almost unnaturally polite among themselves, while each developed defence mechanisms in the fight against boredom. Deane-Drummond lived for escape, though they all realized there was no hope of a successful break while they remained in isolation. Tag Pritchard studied German and tried, with violent exercise, to keep his weight down, for the food at least was plentiful. Chris Lee turned his hand and mind to solving complicated mathematical problems, while George spent his time reading, pacing up and down the ninety-foot walk, looking at the peak of the mountain that rose behind the camp, and in the evenings trying to pick up a little Italian from Lucky.

Under such circumstances anything that broke the routine was welcome, even the visit they had from two German Luftwaffe officers. They both spoke excellent English (one in fact had been to Oxford) and they brought with them a bottle of Scotch.

'Come in, come in,' was the cheerful greeting when George took his turn at being interviewed. 'Sit down and let me pour you a drink.'

He took one, and cheerfully joined with them in condemning the Fascists both as soldiers and captors. There was obviously little love lost between the Germans and their Italian allies.

'It's too bad that you're not in one of our camps,' continued the Luftwaffe officer, 'we pride ourselves on behaving correctly.'

Paterson took this with a large grain of salt and when they turned the talk to his parachute training, parried each question by protesting at the way they were being treated at Sulmona and demanding that his interrogators should do something to improve the situation.

They didn't press him hard and finally, still polite, dismissed him.

'I don't really think they were out for information,' concluded Tag afterwards. 'Probably came to size us up as paratroopers.'

Several weeks passed before they had another visitor, this time a more welcome one. It was on a dreary wet afternoon, with clouds hanging low over the camp and hiding the mountain-top, when the door to their quarters opened and a heavily built man in civilian clothes walked in.

'Good afternoon, gentlemen,' he greeted them in a midwestern twang. 'I'm Colonel Fisk from the American Embassy in Rome. We've got the job, as neutrals, of seeing that you men are being fairly treated. I guess you've got a few complaints that I could take up for you,' he added with a grin.

They had.

'We've committed no military crime.'

'By what right are we held in isolation?'

'No room for exercise.'

'No contact with other Commonwealth prisoners.'

'Do you think you could do anything to get us out of here?'

'Well, I'll sure try. The I-ties look upon you guys as a bad lot, but I'll wave the Geneva convention at them when I get back to Rome and it may do some good. You Britishers have got an awful lot of their boys in the bag, so

I don't think the Fascists would like any bad reports to go out on the way they're treating their prisoners.'

Whether the Colonel's representations carried weight, or whether the Italians had got over their annoyance about the loss of the aqueduct, they did not know, but one morning Fish Eyes, who had done his best during the past months to irritate them with minor restrictions, arrived with a file of soldiers.

'You are being moved to the officers' compound,' he told them in his surliest manner, 'but try any tricks up there and you'll be back in solitary.'

'Oh, go to hell,' snapped George.

Life was better in the new quarters. The compound contained six or seven big dormitory huts, together with a reasonable amount of exercise space, but even more important, there were over a hundred Commonwealth officers, and the new faces and new friendships acted like a tonic on the paratroopers. George was allotted a bed in a hut that went by the imposing title of Dominion House as it contained Australians, New Zealanders, South Africans, British, and now, with Geoff Jowett and himself, Canadians.

Pleasant as this new life was, George soon discovered that the occupants of the hut were living under a cloud. Each of them was allowed half a litre of wine a day. It had become the custom for dormitories to save this ration until a good supply had been built up, and then throw a party for the rest of the compound, but in this obligation of hospitality, Dominion House had failed miserably. Three times they had sent out invitations, but on each occasion, the day before the party, they had succumbed to temptation and drunk the wine themselves.

'We've bloody well got to do better this time,' lectured Bob Ross, a hard-bitten Australian who possessed both a ukulele and an impressive collection of bawdy ballads, when they gathered to discuss the problem. 'Let's agree to save the booze for two weeks and then we'll put on a first-class binge. None of you buggers can be trusted, so we'll make Paterson wine secretary. He's new here and hasn't been corrupted yet.'

Led by Ross, the twenty-odd inhabitants of Dominion House swore by all they held sacred that wine would not pass their lips within the next fortnight, while George was unanimously confirmed as custodian.

All went well this time in preparation for the great soirée. Invitations were sent out and accepted while the buckets, which George stowed under his bed for safekeeping, steadily filled.

After twelve days disaster struck. George had gone out for exercise and on his return discovered eight or ten of his room-mates had cracked under this sobriety and were busy trying to drink the buckets dry. What really shook his faith in human nature was that Bob Ross, who had so eloquently preached temperance, was far and away the drunkest of the lot.

'Why, you lousy bums,' he roared, hastily summoning aid to drive them off, but it seemed that he had arrived too late.

'What the hell are we going to do now?' asked a disgruntled infantry lieutenant. 'There's not enough vino left for the party and we just can't cancel another one.'

The sober members of the hut gloomily pondered this problem and finally Geoff Jowett came up with a suggestion. 'There's a couple of dozen bottles of Bay Rum Hair Tonic in the canteen.'

'So what?'

'It's got an alcohol base. Maybe we could use it to spike the wine we have.'

It was a council of desperation that decided to corner the market in hair tonic. Mixed with their remaining supplies it made a drink with a somewhat unusual flavour, but after a certain amount of sampling Dominion House decided it was fit for human consumption.

On the big night their first guest was Commander Williamson, a gallant and very proper naval officer.

'Good evening, sir,' welcomed George, 'can I get you a drink?'

'That would be delightful, Paterson.'

Filling a tin mug from the nearest bucket, the Canadian passed it to him.

'Bottoms up,' saluted the sea dog and emptied the mug.

Then before George's fascinated gaze a remarkable thing happened. Williamson's complexion, normally a healthy tan, began to manifest chameleon characteristics, turning a rather sickly grey and finally fixing on a blend in which green predominated. At the same time his normally alert eyes became glassy and, mumbling an incoherent excuse, he bolted to the nearest bathroom.

Puzzled, Paterson investigated to see if the trouble could be in their punch. It was. The mixture hadn't been stirred for some time and the wine had sunk to the bottom of the bucket. The Commander had unwittingly downed half a pint of the purest Bay Rum Hair Tonic.

CHAPTER FOUR

DURING these months, escape was a word and a course of
action that loomed large in the minds of many, but escape
from Sulmona, four hundred miles from the Swiss frontier,
was considered almost impossible. Several had got away
from the camp only to be recaptured within a few days,
either betrayed by the local peasants or rendered careless
by hunger, thirst and exhaustion. One officer, who spoke
fluent Italian, had made it by feigning illness and getting
himself removed to Pescara Hospital for observation. Here
he managed to slip away, board a train for Milan, change
there for Como and then walk across the frontier. But he
had the language, and for those who did not the chances
were rather slim.

One day as they strolled together, Garrad-Cole, a fighter
pilot with whom George had become friendly, asked him,
'Would you like to come in on an escape attempt?'

George caught his breath. Escape. For him it symbolized
action and excitement, possibly freedom. 'You're damn
right I would, Garry.'

Cole had got away once before, together with a naval
lieutenant, and they had reached the Adriatic before being
picked up trying to steal a boat. 'The project is well under
way, but I've got permission to bring you in on it. We're
digging a tunnel from the top washroom, right out under
the wire. Come on up and I'll show you.'

Together they sauntered up the compound to the washroom hut, Cole quietly outlining the plan. In a broom
closet off the washroom, some floor tiles had been removed
and, looking down, George saw a dark, narrow shaft.

'They're working in there now,' explained Garrad-Cole, 'and the soil is passed up to these chaps.' He indicated several waiting officers. 'Their job is to wander about outside and dribble it out from their pockets so it won't be noticed. If there's an alarm, the tiles are slapped back into position and we're all busy having a wash. So far the I-ties haven't twigged, and two more weeks should do the job.'

During the next ten days George was kept busy, either wandering aimlessly about among the dormitories, letting the soil that filled his pockets trickle down his trouser legs like sand in an hour glass, or scrounging wood, any wood that could be used to shore up the tunnel roof. Then, early on the eleventh day, fortunately before they began digging, there was a great commotion in the compound. A squad of Carabinieri marched in, cleared the washroom of a group of men only half through their morning shave, and within a matter of minutes had the tunnel entrance opened.

'Some God-damned informer,' growled Cole, 'that's always the way in a big scheme with a lot of people in it. Word always seems to leak out somehow. Lucky though that no one was down there. It's thirty days in isolation for an escape attempt.'

The Italian guards were jubilant as they surveyed the gloomy groups of men who casually strolled past, and soon the story of how the tunnel had been discovered came out. Not informers as they had first thought, not even a slip of someone's tongue but instead, of all things, a mule. The animal, heavily loaded with supplies from Sulmona market, was being led up the path just outside the camp wall, when suddenly the earth gave way and the poor beast disappeared. The nearest guard noticed this phenomenon from his watch-tower, reported it, and within a few minutes the shaft, which had taken so many weary weeks in construction, was discovered.

There was a terrible sense of let-down among the escape group and George, now in his seventh month of captivity, was angry and frustrated. It would take months to dig a new tunnel and meanwhile all that lay ahead was another cold dreary winter.

'Let's see if we can't borrow some wine,' he suggested to Bob Ross a few nights later. 'I need a drink.'

They foregathered in Garrad-Cole's quarters, were soon joined by two pilots, Danny and Ian, together with Neil, a young naval midshipman. As the evening progressed, with Ross and his ukulele providing music of a sort, their mood brightened and through an alcoholic haze even escape seemed less difficult.

'This tunnelling is no good,' Cole said. 'Too slow and too many in the know. There must be a better way out.'

George nodded wisely and somewhat unsteadily replenished his mug. 'You're absolutely right, Garry. We need something quick and unexpected. What about the six of us making a bolt for it on the next organized walk?'

Once a week the officers, under a fairly heavy guard, were allowed out on a country walk, but the idea of breaking away and running for it across fairly open fields while the Carabinieri took pot-shots at them, had long since been considered and discarded by sober, clear-thinking prisoners. The group in Cole's room, however, were at that moment neither sober nor clear-thinking.

'By God, it might work,' decided Danny. 'We could have the rest kick up a row just as we ran for it and that would help get the I-ties rattled.'

'The best place would be where those drainage ditches run across the fields,' cut in Neil. 'They'd be dry at this time of year and once in them you'd be safe from rifle fire. I'll gamble on it if the rest of you are willing.'

With fine enthusiasm, and much clinking of mugs, they agreed to try on the next walk three days hence, and it proved for each of them a long three days. On the following morning the plan didn't seem so good. In fact, the more they considered it on their own, the more foolhardy it appeared, but none cared to back out after all the bold words of the previous night.

Tuesday and Wednesday passed with mounting tension among the six. The escape committee had been approached and had given a somewhat reluctant approval. A number of officers had been brought into the secret and had undertaken to create a small riot at the critical moment of the break.

On Thursday after lunch they set out, fifty or sixty officers with Fish Eyes and a dozen Carabinieri keeping them under watchful surveillance.

As they straggled along the side road, past occasional cottages, scattered olive groves and drab-looking vegetable fields, George could feel his stomach tighten and knot at the unpleasant prospect of a bullet in the back. A glance at Cole's set face told him that he was not the only one prey to dismal thoughts.

'This must be something like a firing squad at dawn,' whispered Garry with a bleak smile.

Now they could see the ditches, across a field just ahead. There would be a run of sixty or seventy yards before they could get near cover. Pray God the guards proved too excited to shoot straight.

He braced himself as he had used to do back in Kelowna getting ready for the hundred-yard dash at the school track meeting. Now was the moment, but still no signal. Had something gone wrong in the plan?

'Let's go,' roared a voice ahead, and shedding every thought but the necessity of reaching the ditch alive, he bolted out of the column and raced across the field. Ten yards. Twenty. And still no shot. Slightly to his left he could see Garry and up ahead to the right were the other

41

four running madly, while behind them a wave of noise, shouts, curses and yells in mixed languages came from the road. Crack. The first shot, over to the right. Only twenty yards to go now. He tried to force his legs to move faster, but they could do no better. Another shot, then a ragged volley, and he saw earth spurt up ahead, while over to the right one of the running figures suddenly crumpled to the ground.

Two more steps and he was into the ditch. A second later Cole tumbled down on top of him.

'Let's get the hell out of here,' snapped George, and running crouched over, gasping for breath, they scurried along the ditch which angled away from the road.

After a few hundred yards they paused for breath. Behind them they could still hear the confused clamour of the column and the angry voices of the guards.

'Fish Eyes will be furious,' grinned Cole, panting hard. 'If we make it, he'll be for the Russian Front and that's the last place these bastards want to go.'

George had been surveying ahead. 'This ditch seems to peter out by those olive trees, and there are some men working in the field beyond, but we'll have to chance that they're too frightened or stupid to bother us. We can't stay here much longer.'

'I'm ready, then,' nodded the other.

They worked along the remaining length of ditch to the olive trees. 'They'll hide us from the road,' whispered Cole. 'Now what we have to do is bluff our way past those chaps ahead.'

They started to walk through the grove when suddenly a voice, high-pitched in its excitement, ordered—''alt! 'alt!'

Swinging about they confronted a big, heavy-jowled man, obviously a farmer, who shouted at them in a burst of angry Italian, while his finger twitched on the trigger of a shotgun that was pointed straight at them.

'Oh damn,' gritted George, 'what do we do now?'

'Don't move, whatever else you do,' warned Cole, 'or he'll blast holes in us.'

George stood quiet, knowing they were trapped. Labourers in the next field, attracted by the commotion, were hurrying up.

Closely guarded by these men with their shovels held at the ready to beat them down at any escape attempt, and with the farmer's shotgun unpleasantly close to their backs, they were returned to the waiting column, where Fish Eyes greeted them with a tirade of abuse. Their fellow prisoners murmured consolations.

'Tough break,' sympathized Tag Pritchard, 'and they got poor young Neil,' he added, pointing to the recumbent figure on the ground. 'Luckily it's only a flesh wound.'

'They haven't brought in Danny,' added Lucky. 'I think he got away.'

'That's good,' George replied. 'It'll make those thirty days in the cooler seem a little more worth while.'

This, it proved, was premature optimism. Five days later Danny, gaunt, unshaven, tired and very hungry joined the group in the isolation cells.

'Don't you believe that the country people are for us,' he warned at the first opportunity. 'They're with Mussolini as long as he's winning. I got turned in by trusting a dear old grandmother who couldn't run fast enough to the Carabinieri to collect a reward.'

When they came out of detention thirty days later, winter with its cold and discomfort was closing in on the camp. Even worse was the food. The Fascists were beginning to realize this war would not be the quick and easy triumph they had first thought and had been forced to institute food rationing throughout the country. Prisoners of war were now on the most meagre diet. Their main meal consisted of a couple of slices of black bread and a very

watery vegetable stew that relied on a little grated cheese
to give it what flavour it possessed. The grating and sprink-
ling of this cheese was one of the duties of the messing
officer, a chore that was shared among the lieutenants.
When Tommy Wilkins of the Hussars, a good cavalryman
but a remarkably poor messing officer, had charge, it
almost led to a lynching.

Tommy, out in the kitchen supervising the fair appor-
tioning of the stew, picked up the wedge of Parmesan that
was the day's ration and went from plate to plate, grating a
little on to each. Then the mess orderlies carried them to
the ravenous officers in the next room, who promptly fell
to. A few seconds later there were howls of protest and
Tommy, rushing through, found a hundred of his brother
officers frothing at the mouth.

'I say, what's the matter, chaps?' he shouted over the
uproar.

'Soap, you blithering fool. You grated up a chunk of
yellow soap.'

There was no other food to be had so the angry prisoners
were forced to skim off the melting granules and carry on
eating, savouring the mixture with thoughts of what they
were going to do to Tommy. Sensing public opinion
against him, the Hussar discreetly went into hiding, where
he remained until tempers cooled.

For George the winter passed slowly. There seemed no
immediate prospects of escape and most of his thoughts
were concentrated on the twin problems of food and keeping warm. Red Cross parcels were now coming through
and meant the difference between mere hunger and actual
starvation. He read a great deal, attended some of the
many lectures that were organized and continued learning
Italian. He was far from proficient, but he was beginning
to speak, understand and read the language. One day,
laboriously ploughing through a copy of a Rome news-

paper he noticed a name that caught his attention. With an effort, for there were many words beyond him, he read the news item and a growing understanding of its meaning left him white and shaken.

'Oh, the bastards,' he swore, savage with mounting rage. They had taken little Sgt. Pichi who had been head waiter at the Savoy before he became a Special Service Paratrooper, led him before a Fascist firing squad and shot him, ignoring the fact that he had long been a British subject and calling him a traitor to Italy for his part in their raid.

'He had guts, and he sure hated dictators,' declared Geoff Jowett when they discussed the tragedy, and possibly Pichi, who had been proud to wear the blue wings of the paratroopers, wouldn't have wanted any other eulogy.

To the prisoners almost any change that broke the soul-destroying monotony of camp life was welcome and in February, after a year's captivity, Paterson got such a change. He and the other Special Force officers, together with Garrad-Cole, Commander Brown and one or two others, were paraded before the Colonello who told them that they were the worst offenders, who were at the bottom of most of the escape plots being hatched and that he was shipping them off to another camp.

After a long and closely guarded journey north they arrived at San Romano on the banks of the Arno between Florence and Pisa. It was an ancient stone monastery, one section of which was still inhabited by monks while the other, walled off and well patrolled, contained forty or fifty captive Greek officers. These, by Anglo-Saxon standards, were a somewhat dirty and dishevelled lot and their quarters were utterly filthy, but they greeted the British amicably enough, and the two groups settled down to live in harmony, though there was little contact as a smattering of French and German was all the language they held in common. Their one mutual interest was bridge, which surmounted the conversation difficulty, and Pritchard, for the sake of allied unity, encouraged his officers to play. They were willing enough, for the Greeks, who were receiving Red Cross parcels, always served cocoa and biscuits afterwards, a big attraction for hungry men.

One evening Pritchard and George were playing together. After the last rubber, as they sat about smiling politely at their hosts and munching biscuits, a young Greek officer came up with a folio of drawings, his own work which he wanted them to admire. Chuckling slyly, he turned over the pages, displaying sketches of naked men and women that were remarkable only for their pornography.

George, knowing Tag's distaste for this sort of thing, noticed with secret amusement his superior writhing in his chair.

'Remember, sir,' he cautioned smugly, 'we must work for allied unity.'

The idea of escape held, as always, a prominent place in their hopes and thoughts. During their first weeks in San Romano they thoroughly examined their section of the building, only to discover that every conceivable exit was well covered by rifle and machine-gun. This left unexplored the monks' side of the monastery which was separated from them by bricked-off corridors. Here, Lucky did some valuable reconnaissance work. Proclaiming himself a Roman Catholic, he demanded that he be allowed to attend services in the chapel at the other end of the building, and after some debate permission was granted. Always under heavy guard he went back and forth, reporting on what he saw to George who, as a former engineer, was detailed to develop an accurate plan of the whole structure. Finally, after weeks of these observations they found that a corridor at the back of their quarters led, or rather would lead, were it not for the brick wall built at its end, straight into a little-used cloister.

'It shouldn't be too difficult to work out a few bricks and make a hole that we could get through,' said Chris Lee when they met to discuss a plan. 'Then, if we did it at night when the monks are asleep in their cells, we could just walk through the monastery and out the gate.'

'What about the Greeks?' cautioned Garrad-Cole. He was thinking, as they all were, about the warning they had received from one of them. 'Most of us hate the Germans and Italians, but we have a few collaborators who will betray you if they get the chance.'

There was a long, thoughtful pause which George finally broke. 'What about giving a party for them like the one they threw on St. George's Day. There would be enough singing and shouting to cover up any noise from the wall.'

The Greek officers had saved both Red Cross parcels and their wine ration for several weeks in order to hold a big celebration in honour of St. George, patron saint of both England and Greece. Now this hospitality could be returned because their own Red Cross parcels had caught up with them. At the same time a party would ensure that no one outside the plan would be likely to visit the back corridor on the night of their break.

'That's the ticket,' decided Commander Brown, the senior among them. 'We'll start saving wine and food right away. Deane-Drummond and I will get out the bricks while you others play host. We'll give you a sign when we're ready and then it's Switzerland, God willing.'

During the next couple of weeks they were kept busy with secret preparations. Clothes, especially those that had been purchased since their capture, had to be shared out and often altered to give them some appearance of being civilians. Identity cards that might pass a cursory inspection were painstakingly forged. Money was saved and routes planned. Then it was the morning of the day, a day that slowly dragged through to evening.

I wonder if we've missed anything, worried George as he played the jovial host and did his best to intoxicate the guests while remaining sober himself. One or other would occasionally leave the mess to return a few moments later with a report on how the work was going.

'It's a devilish job, breaking this mortar without making too much noise,' Brown told him when it was his turn to slip back, 'but we've got one brick out and we should be ready in another hour or so.'

By now the party was in full swing and sometime later when word came back that the hole was nearly big enough the British officers were able to slip away unnoticed. They ran to their rooms and hastily began to get ready when suddenly to their horror, Brown and Deane-Drummond came rushing down the corridor.

'It's all up,' shouted Brown angry with frustration. 'Some bloody monk heard a brick drop and came to investigate. He went off in full voice yelling for the guard and they'll be round here in a couple of minutes. Hide everything incriminating and get to bed.'

Five minutes later a detachment of Carabinieri headed by an angry lieutenant came to investigate. George was innocently sleeping when they entered his room, and when they made him understand that there had been an escape attempt, protested long and loudly against the injustice of suspecting him. They were almost convinced and just about to complete their search when one of them lifted the linoleum covering his bedside table and revealed a complete set of plans of the monastery.

Ah well, he philosophized as they marched him off to the isolation cells, a month's quiet will do me good. As it turned out though, he had plenty of company—all the British officers, except two. These two, who had somehow managed to convince the Italians of their innocence, were Commander Brown and Tony Deane-Drummond.

Months passed enlivened by only one incident out of the ordinary. Deane-Drummond managed to escape. He feigned mastoid trouble and was moved to Florence Military Hospital for observation where one night he slipped past his guard, caught a dawn train for Milan, then on to Como and over the border. Though they knew when he left them that he had a good plan, a discreetly worded postcard from Geneva was their first sure knowledge of this success. Much later they learned that he had crossed into France with several other escapees and, guided by the French underground, had reached a lonely beach a score of miles from Marseilles where a small British naval vessel, disguised as a Spanish fishing boat, had come in late one night and taken them off.

This escape and their previous unsuccessful attempt made them extremely unpopular with the Italian officers who knew that a successful break out of San Romano might exile them to the Russian Front. They became excessively suspicious and unpleasant in their attitude. It was almost a relief in the late summer when the commandant called them into his office and, after the usual reproaches about their ingratitude and lack of co-operation, told them they were being transferred to Gavi, a camp reserved for the most unruly officer prisoners and reputed to be escape-proof.

Gavi was twenty miles north of Genoa, an ancient walled fortress built high up on the side of a mountain, approached by only one narrow winding road from the valley. On almost every side there were precipitous drops, while the walls bristled with machine-gun posts and patrolling sentries.

No wonder they call it escape-proof, thought George gloomily after his first look around. By now he had been eighteen months in captivity and, if not resigned to his condition, he had at least learned how to live with it. The chief problem was to fill in each day with exercise—volley ball was the popular game—with reading or with learning something, no matter whether it was German, Italian, applied mathematics or early Chinese art. Just so long as it kept one busy without too much time to brood. Then there was the dramatic club with young naval midshipmen being conscripted for the feminine roles and, most popular of all, the casino where large-scale gambling provided the only excitement allowed them. Here poker, bridge, roulette, faro, baccarat and a host of other games were played, sometimes for very high stakes, with the losses being paid by cheque on English banks. At least one officer won a small fortune, but even for those who lost, the play added zest to the otherwise dreary days.

The seasons passed monotonously until from the reports of newly arrived prisoners they learnt that the tide had turned. North Africa had been won, Sicily had been invaded, and then suddenly there came news that was a bombshell to both guards and prisoners. Mussolini, the would-be Caesar, had fallen and was under arrest, while the new government was suing for peace.

'It's all over. It's all over,' shrieked an excited Italian soldier. 'Soon we can go home.'

Machine-gun posts were deserted, sentry boxes left unoccupied as captors and captives mingled in a frenzy of congratulations. Wine was brought up from the stores and soon all were busy celebrating the end of the long travail.

Prisoners could have walked out through the unguarded gates, but they had received word via a secret channel that if Italy fell they should remain collected together in their camps for ease in repatriation.

However, next morning, after the first flush of enthusiasm had worn off, many of them had doubts about this policy and the sight of the guards once more at their usual stations increased these doubts. Looking down towards the village in the valley they suddenly realized the reason for this return of vigilance. A German unit, distinctive in its field-grey uniforms, had moved in during the night.

'They say they will shoot us if we let you go,' wailed one unhappy Italian.

Word of this disaster to their hopes quickly spread through the compounds, bringing gloom at the thought of yesterday's wasted opportunity.

For a few weeks camp life returned to near normal, but with the German unit remaining in the village below to keep the Italians on their toes. Several unco-ordinated escape attempts were made during this period, but only one was successful: a batman got away hidden in a load of garbage.

Early in September the Germans, a hard-bitten lot, moved in, dismissing the Fascist garrison with open contempt. At the evening meal the prisoners were ordered to be ready for a move early the following morning. This looked like a trip to Germany, the last place George wanted to go, but what could he do? Casting about desperately he came up with an idea. In the morning there would be a lot of confusion and if he could hide somewhere his absence might not be noticed. Then, after the fortress had been evacuated, he could slip out and take his chance hiding in the countryside.

He knew just the place in which to conceal himself, the rafters of a small coal shed behind the cookhouse.

A couple of hours after lights out he crept in and climbed up to a precarious and uncomfortable perch. With any sort of luck this should work, he decided.

It might have worked had not a lot of other officers had exactly the same idea. 'One hundred and seventeen prisoners not accounted for,' reported the German sergeant-major after roll call.

'Have the place searched,' the Commandant ordered curtly, and squads were quickly detailed for the hunt. Slowly they moved from building to building hooting with laughter as they hauled out cursing men from cupboards, attics, disused storerooms and myriad other hiding-places. Finally, late in the afternoon, the last of them was winkled out and herded on to the square.

'Because of your stupid behaviour the move is postponed until tomorrow morning,' stormed the Commandant, 'and I would warn you gentlemen that any further attempts at concealment will be punished severely.'

Next day they were lined up for the customary search before being loaded on to the waiting trucks.

'All prisoners to strip,' came the order and they and their clothes were closely examined by a fat, pompous-looking lieutenant.

'Bend over,' came the next command, and he strolled along behind examining their rectums for concealed maps, codes or other paraphernalia of escape. Suddenly he stopped behind an armoured corps captain who was noted for his sense of humour.

'Ach, what have we here,' the officer squealed excitedly in a voice that drew every eye towards him. Carefully, very carefully, he drew out a thin roll of paper from the captain's posterior and, flourishing it triumphantly, marched over to the nearest table, certain that this would mean promotion, possibly a medal from the Führer.

Slowly unrolling his find, while prisoners and guards watched in fascinated curiosity he read two boldly pencilled words, 'Heil Hitler'.

It was to be their last laugh for a long time. Angrily the search was concluded. They were ordered to dress and hurried to waiting vehicles. Impatiently the Commandant waved the signal from the head of the line; motor-cycle outriders kicked their machines into life, truck engines roared and their convoy bristling with armed guards, began to roll down the road to the east.

All day they travelled across Northern Italy, silent and depressed in the knowledge that after being so near to freedom they were now worse off than ever.

Once we're in Germany there'll be damn all chance of making a break, reflected George. We'll be there till the end of the war, and God knows how many years that will be.

This sense of hopeless desperation pervaded them all, especially Porky, a big South African infantry lieutenant.

In the early afternoon they suddenly noticed that the trucks ahead were swinging through the gate of a big Luftwaffe aerodrome and Porky, when he saw this, was certain that his last chance had come.

'Oh man, they're flying us to the Fatherland.' With that, just as their vehicle was turning in, he dived over the side, unfortunately landing on his head. Half a dozen gate guards were on him in an instant like a rugger scrum, and a couple of minutes later Porky dazed, bleeding and manacled, was returned to his truck in disgrace.

'Next time we shoot,' warned their keepers.

Porky's immediate fears were soon dispelled as the stop was only to refuel. Soon the convoy continued on its way. Towards evening they pulled into the freight yards of a big city, Mantua, and were unceremoniously urged into a goods warehouse, already half filled with several hundred gloomy prisoners who had arrived earlier in the day from other camps.

'We're supposed to leave tomorrow,' a New Zealander said. 'They're going to freight us in over the Brenner Pass to God knows where. Poland or East Germany is my guess.'

That night George slept fitfully on the dirty concrete floor. His dreams were nightmares and when he woke the reality seemed worse. For two and a half dreary years he had always had some hope, no matter how small, but now all hope seemed gone.

CHAPTER FIVE

T H E door of their freight car slid shut and they heard the lock turn. There was the crunch of cinders and gravel as the two German guards moved along the train and they were left in the hot half-darkness, each man alone with his thoughts.

'Oh Christ, what bloody luck,' groaned a voice from the corner, but no one bothered to answer. They just lay sprawled beside their few possessions, hopeless in their misery.

There had been hours outside in the dusty station yard under heavy guard. The hot September sun beating down had made them feel faint and dry, while the slow business of counting, recounting and herding the hundreds of prisoners into cars had continued. It was a long train with more than thirty locked box cars, each filled with human freight interspersed by open vans for the S.S. troopers with their sub-machine-guns. Now they were loaded and ready for an unknown destination somewhere in the Fatherland.

At last they heard a distant whistle from ahead and a few moments later their train, after some initial jerks and bumps came to life. George glanced at his watch; the phosphorescent hands pointed at a quarter to six. Then he lapsed back into dormant apathy.

For more than an hour they made good time rumbling north across the plain, but as their engine began to breast the first of the foothills the pace slackened perceptibly. Now hunger also began to rouse them from listless dejection. Men sat up in the darkness and started rummaging through packs for chocolate, biscuits, raisins or other Red Cross supplies they had managed to bring with them from

Gavi. After hunger, the urge to escape reasserted itself. Frankie and Johnnie, two South Africans, one English, the other Boer, put it into words.

'There must be a way out of this goddamn wooden box.'

'Ja,' echoed Johnnie. 'Maybe we could force the door.'

They tried, but the lock held firm.

'I wonder if we could cut a hole through the wall?' suggested Frankie. 'It's heavy planking but worth a try. Anybody manage to bring along a knife?'

A whip round of concealed items revealed a small pocket knife while Johnnie proudly produced something he had purloined before leaving camp, a pair of heavy duty dental pliers with an end hooked like a parrot's beak.

'Maybe we use these?' he asked.

They went to work at the front end of the car using the knife to cut into the wood, then inserting the hooked pliers to tear out strips. It was slow work, but after an hour they had cut and torn a small hole through to the outside, and with this proof that it might work, the whole van became electric with excitement. Then, as though fate was determined to go against them, the train began to slow, and finally halted.

'Quick,' snapped George, 'stuff this sweater in the hole. It's almost dark out and the guards will never notice.'

They tensed as two soldiers, talking softly together in German, came to the car, checked the door and moved on. For fifteen minutes they waited, sick with apprehension in case some sentry should think of checking between the cars, but nothing happened and finally, after a fast-moving express had roared past, they once again pulled out on to the main line.

'All right, fellows,' ordered Frankie, 'let's get cracking.'

They worked in pairs, cutting, chipping, tearing feverishly and as the opening grew giving them more room they were able to make much better progress in ripping out the wood. Three times more their train was forced into sidings to clear the line for more important traffic, but a coat draped over the hole hid it from prying eyes.

By midnight the opening was large enough for a man to squeeze through and they began to prepare for escape, filling their pockets with food and any cigarettes they had. The plan was to go in pairs, wriggling out on to the coupling and then moving over to the buffers, one on each side, ready to jump when the train slowed on an uphill incline.

Frankie and Johnnie, who had sparked the scheme, would go first while the others drew straws. George found himself, along with an unknown partner, third on the list immediately following Mike and Peter, two Yugoslav officers with unpronounceable names.

The South Africans got away successfully, and then Mike and Peter, both voluble and excited, clambered out. George, next in line, stuck his head through the opening to watch their progress as he waited his own turn. For what seemed an interminable time they were on a flat stretch, running through a mountain valley at too high a speed for jumping. Minutes passed before they again hit the upgrade and the cars began to slow. Peter braced himself and leapt outwards and George started to clamber out to take his place. Just as he was almost out on the coupling, the train gave a sudden jerk and Mike, losing his balance, fell backwards and down. There was one terrible shriek as the wheel did its deadly work and Paterson, frozen with horror, clung to the jagged edge of the hole willing himself not to be sick.

It was several minutes before those behind, unaware of the tragedy, roused him. 'For Christ's sake get moving, George, or we'll never get out at this speed.'

He reached the buffer, dimly aware that his partner was on the other side, and waited. They were on a downhill run now, picking up speed; it would be suicide to jump.

He held on grimly, shuddering as he thought of that body toppling backwards.

Seven or eight minutes went by before the train began to slow again. The speed dropped quickly and when he judged it was down to about twenty he braced himself and leapt outwards, landing with a skin-scraping crash on the gravelled track.

The momentum rolled him forward a number of feet and then he lay still, winded and a little dazed, but knowing that he must not move. The train was still slowing, creaking and groaning against the pressure of the brakes. He felt a chill of fear in case a guard on one of the flat cars should notice him and open up with a burst of automatic fire. The freight cars were only crawling past now and it took an effort of will to keep still and not glance up to see what was happening. He was going to be in a hell of a mess if it stopped right beside him.

Finally he heard the caboose go by no faster than a man could run, and saw with relief its red tail light moving away along the track.

His relief was short-lived. Just as he was about to sit up and brush the dirt and gravel from his skinned hands, the train, with a final protesting squeal of iron wheels, halted no more than eighty yards ahead. Almost immediately bursts of rifle and semi-automatic fire sprayed back along the line.

Oh blast, they saw me, was his first thought as he hugged the ground, but as the shots continued he realized that they were over his head, aimed further back.

There was no sign or sound of his jumping partner, but maybe he'd been seen. Actually he was to discover more than a year later it was neither of them who had caused the fireworks. Officers in other cars had also been at work. In at least three the doors had been forced and it was the men jumping from one of these that had been seen.

Lying there Paterson did some quick thinking. Any movement might reveal his presence and draw fire, but at any moment now a party of Germans might be sent back along the track where they couldn't help but notice him. He decided he had to start moving and the sooner the better. On the right the land sloped up towards a bare mountainside and to the left, down the embankment, there was a scrub-covered hillside that ended in a broad river. This was the best chance he decided, and cautiously slithering over the track, he rolled down the slope and into the cover of undergrowth.

Apparently he had not been seen, for no shots came his way. Picking himself up and running crouched over, he moved fast down the hill away from the train. Branches scratched and tore him, but he scarcely noticed them in the desperate urgency to put space between himself and any pursuers. Only when he reached the river some way down, did he feel reasonably safe from pursuit and slow his pace to a walk while he debated his next move. It would be best he reasoned to get over the river. He would have to swim it, but then he could work away from the railway.

Stripping, he made a bundle of his boots and clothing and strapped it to a piece of wood that he found wedged against the bank. Then he waded in, gasping as the cold mountain water hit his hot, perspiring skin. A few steps and he was swimming, pushing the clothing before him. Now the river seemed wider and the current stronger than he had first thought. It caught him up and swept him downstream, but slowly he made progress, gradually edging in towards the opposite bank. He would make it he knew, but only just. Then an eddy caught at his bundle of clothing and tore it out of his numbed grasp and swept it away. He made a desperate attempt to recover it, but it bobbed out of reach. Too tired really to care, he half swam, half crawled the last few feet and collapsed on the bank to regain his breath.

After a few minutes he sat up and couldn't help grinning as he considered his position. He was on the run in hostile country without a stitch of clothing. He would have to get clothes somewhere, but the first thing was to leave the river behind. It was dark and silent except for the distant barking of a dog as he limped through the vineyards acutely conscious of his nakedness. For more than an hour he went on until, weary and badly in need of sleep, with the night air becoming unpleasantly chill on his skin, he looked for shelter. There was a small village over on his left and near at hand through the trees, he could discern what looked like a farmhouse. Approaching cautiously and thanking God that no snarling mongrel rushed out to greet him, he reconnoitred the silent building. There was an open basement window. After a few moments' indecision he lowered himself down through it.

The basement itself was very dark, but it seemed to be used to store vegetables and groping around he found a pile of empty sacks. They seemed more inviting than any spring-filled mattress. Pulling a few over him, he let his tired body become limp and relaxed.

Footsteps on the floor above woke him, but it was some little time before he could shake off the warm drowsiness of sleep and remember what had happened. Outside the dark had turned to the greyness of approaching dawn. Before people were about in the nearby village he must get clothes and help, and those upstairs were as likely to assist as any others. Resolved on a course of action, he threw off the sacks, wriggled back out through the window and fell to shivering in the cold morning air. There was a clothesline behind the house with a couple of sheets on it. Pulling off one he draped it around himself like a toga and hammered on the back door.

For a few moments nothing happened and he repeated his knock. Then there were footsteps, the sound of a bolt being drawn, and the door was swung open by a dark-haired, sturdily built teenage girl.

'Signorina,' he began in his best Italian, but got no further. The sight of so much young manhood draped in one of their best sheets was too much for the girl. With a shriek she disappeared down the passage in a flurry of skirts, and he could hear her voice constantly rising in its excitement, coming from somewhere inside the house.

Presently an older woman came forward a little diffidently, ready to run if he made any untoward move.

'Signora,' he began hurriedly, 'I'm an escaped Canadian prisoner. I need clothes and food. Can you help me?'

She considered the question for a time, not unsympathetic but very frightened. 'You had better go to the priest,' she said finally. 'He will know what is best. My daughter will show you the way.'

With the girl, now more curious than frightened, guiding him, he was led along the village street, silent and grey in the half-light. It was still deserted, but lights were beginning to come on in the houses. At one his guide knocked and an elderly housekeeper confronted them.

'I'm an escaped prisoner,' began George, while the girl amplified in voluble Italian. The woman grasped the situation, beckoned him in and quickly shut the door. Then she took him into a small, austere room, bare of any decoration save for a crucifix on the wall, where an elderly, grey-haired and rather shabbily dressed priest was having his breakfast.

George told his story while the other listened attentively. He seemed friendly but very nervous.

'You couldn't stay here,' he said at last. 'The Germans are in the next village and they would soon find out, but

I'll go and visit my people and get you some clothes. The Signora will give you a meal while I am gone.'

He was back in half an hour with a bundle of assorted male attire, all a little short and tight on a six-foot-three frame but nevertheless wearable. Only the boots were utterly impossible.

'I can't get into these,' George confessed ruefully after several attempts. 'Do you think you could find a larger pair?'

Clicking his tongue thoughtfully the little priest set off again, returning this time with what were undoubtedly the oldest and shabbiest pair of boots in the village. The inner soles were cracked and rough, a warning of trouble to come, but at least they fitted, if somewhat snugly.

'Come,' said the priest, obviously relieved to see the last of so dangerous a guest, 'and I'll show you your way.' At the door he pointed westward towards a range of hills that stretched into the distance. 'Beyond them is Lake Garda. You will have to go round the north end, then work south-west. In that way there are passes that lead over the mountains into Switzerland, but you have a long journey my son, and may God be with you.'

All that day under a warm September sun he walked across the wild and rugged hills, sometimes in upland meadows, at others in the shade of beech woods, until late in the afternoon he came to the edge of the high ground and looked down over prosperous farms and vineyards to the blue waters of the lake sparkling in the distance. His way now led along a ridge that ran parallel to the plain. He followed it for several miles, his pace slowing. The exhilaration that had come with the first hours of freedom was gone and now he was tired, footsore and most of all, hungry.

'If I could find another priest, maybe I could get some dinner and a bed,' he reflected.

Ahead, nestling at the foot of the hills, lay a village with a church on its outskirts. The afternoon was turning into evening with the shadows growing long as he came down from the high ground. There had been a service for as he neared the church a small congregation straggled out and dispersed towards the village. He waited, loitering aimlessly and in a few moments the priest, well fed and prosperous looking, came out. Paterson promptly cornered him.

'Padre,' he began, 'I'm a Canadian officer escaping from the Germans and I need food. Will you help me?'

The cleric's eyes were cold and hostile in his fleshy face. 'I can't. You'd better leave here immediately.'

The look and the tone suggested that this meeting would be reported to the nearest Carabinieri, so George lost no time putting the village and its inhospitable pastor as far behind him as possible. That night, hungry and cold, he slept under the shelter of a clump of bushes on a bare hillside.

The next day was a repetition of the first, only worse. He needed food and he was thirsty, yet there were few streams where he could drink, and his feet, blistered and cut, seemed to hurt more with every step. In the afternoon an old woman in a shepherd's hut gave him some bread and milk. That night he once again slept out, not daring to take off his boots, for his feet were swelling and he knew that he would never get them back on.

Morning found him gaunt and unshaven. His stomach was aching with hunger and he had a growing feeling that even recapture would be better than this. He sat for a long time before summoning up the will to move, but finally stumbled to his feet. I'll starve up here, he thought; better head down for a road and take my chance. Maybe I can find a monastery and get shelter.

The going was much easier along the highway and he

helped himself to bunches of grapes from the vineyards that lined the way. They did a little, but not much, to quench thirst and ease hunger. What obsessed him as he tramped along in the gathering heat was a longing for beer —lots of it, cold and foaming. He licked dry, cracked lips and forced his mind back to the present situation. By now it was noon and he couldn't go much longer without rest. But where? As long as he kept moving, the men and women working in the fields and the passing traffic, much of it German, never gave him a second glance, but once he lay down by the roadside he would arouse curiosity. Finally a big dry culvert, into which he crawled and stretched out, solved his problem.

He lay there for several hours while the traffic rumbled overhead. For a time he slept but woke with a start, fancying himself still in the freight car heading for Germany. It was nearly three now; the heat was less and it was time to start moving. Scrambling out and brushing the dirt from his ragged trousers, he forced his burning, throbbing feet into motion. There was a sign just ahead that read, 'Brescia 5 Kilometres.'

Either I get help there or I've had it, he decided, limping along the verge.

Soon the vineyards began to give way to houses, then there were cross streets and more traffic. This was a fair-sized city, he surmised, as he made his way past squalid rows of houses and dirty, blank-walled warehouses. People were beginning to look at him and take note of his dirty, unshaven condition, his clothes, shabby even by Italian standards, and the way he staggered at times, as though drunk.

He made himself go on trying to appear unconcerned while looking for a church or a monastery where he might gain sanctuary, but there seemed to be none in this district. Then a cyclist passed him and the rider turned to stare as though he had noticed something strange. He braked just ahead and waited until George came up.

He was a small dark man of about thirty, roughly dressed in workman's clothes, with a broad smile that showed flashing white teeth.

'Inglese?' he enquired in a dramatic stage whisper.

Paterson nodded wearily, too tired to care whether this man was friend or foe.

'I have helped another Inglese,' continued the other. 'You follow me and I'll help you.'

Again George nodded and the man set off pedalling slowly, keeping forty or fifty feet ahead. They went down streets and dark alleys that were almost slums until they emerged finally into a dirty, noisy courtyard where small children were playing. A number of doors opened off it.

At one of these the man, who gave his name as Luigi, paused.

'My home,' he explained, ushering George in. There were two women in the small front room, wife and mother-in-law he concluded, as he almost collapsed into a chair.

Under a hail of instructions from the garrulous Luigi, the women began bustling about. The ill-fitting boots were removed and his feet, a bloody mass of burst blisters and sores, were bathed, bandaged and gently put into slippers. The relief was wonderful. And then spaghetti and coarse bread was brought him, and wine. Word of his arrival spread around the courtyard, for, as he ate, the neighbours began crowding in to stare and listen to Luigi's account of their meeting, and to admire his acuteness in spotting the 'Inglese'.

'You are a hero,' he dramatically informed George, 'and we who also hate the German pigs are your friends. Is there anything we can get you?'

Despite the wine he had drunk he was still thirsty with a deep thirst that only one drink could quench. 'I don't sup-

pose there is such a thing as a bottle of beer in this town?'
he asked.

Luigi with an objective was dynamic. 'Leave it to me,'
he promised. 'I will go and find some immediately.'

Half an hour later he was back, triumphantly carrying
two bottles of local beer, light stuff and warm, but George
felt, as it trickled down his throat, that he had never tasted
anything so good. In a drowsy, half-dazed condition he sat
back in the chair and let the babble of conversations that
filled in the little room flow over his head.

Luigi, who was stage-managing the evening and enjoying himself immensely, noticed his fatigue.

'Come,' he said, patting him on the shoulder, 'you can
sleep at my sister-in-law's, next door. Her husband is away
in the army and she will help.'

They went out into the courtyard and in through the
next door. The little front room was empty, but Luigi,
with the familiarity of close relationship strode through to
the bedroom. As they entered there was a startled shriek, a
flurry of bedclothes and a young woman as naked as the
day she was born, leapt out of the bed and fled precipit-
ously through another door while a man equally nude, sat
up in the bed looking somewhat abashed.

For Luigi the whole business was a tremendous joke.

'This is the other Inglese.'

'I'm Corporal Jack Harris,' the man explained, getting
up and pulling on some clothes. 'Been hiding here for the
last five days and these people have been awfully kind to
me.'

'So I see,' commented George dryly as he slumped down
across the bed, too utterly exhausted to care about anything but sleep.

CHAPTER SIX

'I DON'T like the situation,' George commented to Jack Harris as they squatted on the doorstep and watched the community life of the courtyard. 'Luigi's a good fellow, but...'

It was five days since he had come to stay with Angelina, the young lady who had greeted him in such an unorthodox manner. The rest and food had done wonders in rebuilding his strength while his feet, though still tender, were healing and he could walk without pain. Now that he was rested and had time to think of more than food and shelter, the danger in the present set up became increasingly evident.

'He's a good little chap and I like him,' he continued, 'but he talks too much. He hates the Fascists and Nazis and thinks everyone else does. Someone is going to hear him and betray us to the Gestapo and then God help us all. For his sake and our own, we've got to get away.'

Corporal Harris, a muscular young man of twenty-five with his full share of common sense, nodded.

'Yes,' he agreed soberly, 'I've listened to them, and they just don't seem to realize what a dangerous business this is and what's going to happen if they're found out.'

As a prisoner of war he had been sent to work on Italian farms and had come to speak the language fluently.

'I've heard him talking about the partisans,' he went on, 'and maybe we would be better out in the country with one of their bands. What do you think?'

'It's a good idea,' agreed George. 'Maybe we could help them in their raids. I know something about explosives and demolition work, and you could handle a wireless if they had one. Let's have a talk with Luigi.'

Their host was enthusiastic when they broached the idea. 'Splendid, splendid. The Allies will undoubtedly be here in a few weeks and till then you can fight with us. Leave it to me and I'll make all the arrangements.'

Three nights later they set off on bicycles with Luigi as guide. For a few miles they pedalled through the silent countryside and then, leaving their cycles in a derelict shed, they set off at a brisk pace along the rough hill tracks. George, wearing a pair of rope-soled canvas shoes that had been found for him, had no difficulty keeping up. They went on for several hours, sometimes climbing, sometimes dropping down into the valleys, but never it seemed, getting very far from farms or small villages.

'I thought they'd have their camp well away from civilization way up in the hills,' commented Harris.

'So did I,' agreed George, 'but I guess they know their own business.'

A long climb brought them to a small pasture, almost encircled by beechwoods, with a roughly built stone barn to one side.

'Our headquarters,' Luigi informed them proudly.

In the doorway with a rifle across his knee a man sprawled, snoring gently. They shook him awake and with a sleepy grunt he led them inside.

Throwing dry wood on the dying embers of a fire he filled mugs and gave them some rough local wine.

In the firelight they could see about twenty recumbent forms stretched out on the dirt floor and soon most of them, awakened by the new arrivals, were seated about the blaze, yawning and spitting, but obviously well disposed towards them.

Ferrucio their chief, a thin saturnine man in early middle age, felt it incumbent upon his dignity to make a speech of welcome. He was an army deserter, a fanatical Communist party member, but most of all he was an Italian with all that nation's love of dramatic oratory.

'We are proud to have you with us, comrades and soldiers of our glorious allies, and we look upon you as brothers in the sacred cause of liberty,' he began. There was considerably more which Jack Harris, somewhat cynically summed up as 'don't take more than your fair share of the grub and keep your bowels open.'

With the formal welcoming ceremony over and everyone feeling pleasantly drowsy from the wine, the whole party, including the guard, curled up in blankets or coats and went back to sleep.

The next day initiated Paterson and Harris into the ways of these partisans. It was a life that had certain characteristics of a poorly run boys' camp combined with a down-at-heels robber band. Everyone rose when he pleased, breakfast was eaten off dirty dishes, ladled from a community stew pot, and afterwards the plates were cleaned with coarse black bread. As for drink, there seemed to be a plentiful supply of vino. Afterwards if the weather was nice one might stroll through the woods that crowned the hilltop, or lie out in the sunshine. Peasants would trudge up from the valley with supplies of bread, meat or wine, though whether this was paid for or commandeered was uncertain. The band members themselves seemed free to leave or stay as fancy dictated.

'I'm going home for a few days,' one told George with a broad grin, 'to see if my wife is behaving herself.'

Mostly they were little more than schoolboys playing at high adventure along with a few older men, some of them army deserters, others genuine opponents of the régime. But there seemed to be no discipline, no purpose in their organization. At night they sat round the fire, drinking and making wonderful plans for attacking small arms plants, railway stations or police barracks, but they never seemed to get beyond the talking stage and by morning the plans had faded away like mists before the sun.

'We'd better have a look around and see if this place can be defended,' Paterson had said on the first morning, 'and we'd better find out what they have in the way of arms.'

An inconspicuous count showed that the guerrillas possessed seven battered and rusty Italian army rifles and two pistols one of which Ferrucio wore strapped to his waist, more as a picturesque item of attire than anything else. This was not an encouraging figure and several walks round the perimeter of the hill revealed another unsettling fact.

'This place couldn't be held for five minutes,' George confided to Harris. 'We've got no weapons to speak of and half the countryside knows our whereabouts. It's only a matter of time before someone tips off the Huns and they'll send up a platoon to wipe us out.'

They got Ferrucio to one side and tactfully pointed out the danger. He listened politely, but was obviously quite unconcerned.

'Yes, many people do know of this hiding-place, but you don't know Italians. They would sooner die under torture than breathe a word of our whereabouts. As to weapons, you are right. We need many and tonight we will plan how to get them.'

Around the fire that evening they planned, gloriously, nothing less than an attack on the big Carabinieri barracks in Brescia. It seemed a little ambitious, but they were all full of enthusiasm with ideas and suggestions tumbling out in a flood of rhetoric that did not cease until the effects of wine and the lateness of the hour laid them low in their bedrolls.

'We will finish our planning tomorrow,' Ferrucio assured them a little thickly. But next night to George's

amazement, the Carabinieri barracks were completely forgotten and instead there was great talk of blowing up a
railway bridge some twenty miles to the south.

'But you've got no explosives,' he protested.

This was ignored as tactless and socially inept, and the
evening continued unspoilt by reality. Harris nudged him
and winked. 'I think the sooner we get out of here the better.'

This opinion was confirmed several days later when they
returned from an afternoon walk through the beech woods.
They could see as they approached the camp that something was amiss, for the whole band was milling about
talking, shouting and brandishing weapons. And then they
saw Luigi. Apparently he had arrived during their absence
and now presented a most woe-begone appearance. He was
tightly bound to a tree while Ferrucio, in a paroxysm of
fury, waved his pistol threateningly in the other's terrified
face.

'Hold on, hold on,' shouted George, running up.
'What's the trouble?'

'This Fascist dog has betrayed us and he's going to die,'
snarled the furious leader.

Then slowly the story came out, well seasoned with oaths
and blood-curdling threats. Word had got about in Brescia
of their existence and Luigi, as a resident of that city, was
immediately suspect and whether innocent or guilty was to
pay with his life.

'It isn't true. It isn't true,' wailed the unhappy man. 'I
have been as silent as a grave.'

George, knowing his garrulity, rather doubted this but
he was also certain that the little man, though indiscreet,
was no traitor.

'It was through him that we were saved from the Germans,' he argued, 'and he wouldn't have done that if he
had been a Fascist informer.'

It took an hour of hard talk, always with an eye on the waving pistol, before the angry Ferrucio was cool enough to be reasonable.

'Well,' he finally admitted grudgingly, obviously disappointed at being deprived of an execution, 'maybe he's not a traitor, but he talks too damn much and has to be punished. He can stay tied to the tree till morning.'

Luigi, just saved from a horrible death, now raised a new howl.

'Leave me tied to this tree all night? What are you, the Gestapo, that you torture a brave Italian?'

The whole band divided on this, some supporting, others opposing the punishment and all vehemently arguing the case. Finally they reached a compromise with the prisoner being retied sitting down with his back to the tree, where he was left under the care of an armed guard.

Next morning when George awoke he found Luigi peacefully snoring on the straw beside him.

'How the hell did you get in here?' he demanded in surprise, shaking the other awake.

'After the guard went to sleep I just untied the knots.'

'But won't you be in trouble with the band?'

'Trouble? What for?'

George shook his head in absolute perplexity. This was too much like Alice in Wonderland for him. 'Look here,' he said, 'we're leaving, and I want you to help us get to Milan so that we can cross the border.'

In late afternoon after many expressions of mutual esteem, they bade farewell to the partisans and returned to Brescia where Luigi, as eager as a puppy with a new game, assured them that he would soon make the necessary contacts.

Next day there was much activity. Finally the arrangements were completed.

With their host as guide they bicycled through the town

and out into one of the better-class suburbs. In front of a big modern apartment building, a young woman wearing a vivid blue scarf was apparently very busy pumping up her bicycle tyre.

Luigi braked some distance down the street.

'There's your guide,' he said, indicating the girl with a jerk of his head. 'She's going to take you to a hiding-place out in the country and they will help you get to Milan. May the Saints preserve you both.'

Before they could thank him he was gone, pedalling away furiously while the girl, who had noticed them, re-clipped the pump and set off some fifty yards in the lead. They rode on through the suburbs and out into the country past well-tended vineyards and small farms. The October dusk was beginning to close in some half hour later when they swung off the highway on to a side road. They followed this for about a mile.

The girl, indistinct in the twilight, swung through a gate that led to a large, prosperous-looking farmhouse.

Propping her cycle against the wall she knocked while they hung back in the shadows. The door opened and after a few words of conversation she signalled them forward.

'You will be safe here with the Riccinis. Now I must get back to Brescia before my parents begin to worry.'

Signora Riccini and her slim, dark-haired daughter Gabi, greeted them like heroes. 'We will do everything we can to help you escape.'

An old maidservant brought them coffee while they chatted. Afterwards there was an excellent dinner where they met the Signore, a quiet courteous man who seemed more interested running his large farm than in politics which he left to his wife and daughter. But he echoed their offer of hospitality.

'You are welcome in this house as long as you care to stay.'

'You're going to need new clothes,' decided the Signora. 'Those outfits are shocking. We'll have to take you to the tailor who makes all my husband's clothes. He can be trusted. Then we must find a man who can take you to Milan and make the necessary contacts for getting you across the frontier. We've heard of someone in Brescia who may be just the person and we're trying to get in touch with him, but it will probably be a week or so before everything is ready.'

CHAPTER SEVEN

LIFE with the Riccinis was peaceful and pleasant. There were clean sheets on the beds and the food was excellent. Urban Italy might be rationed, but on a big farm there was no shortage. They thought it best to keep inside the house during daylight, but there were books and magazines to read and George, who wanted to improve his command of the language, found a willing teacher in the pretty nineteen-year-old daughter of the house. At dusk when the labourers had gone home to their cottages, they would go for walks usually accompanied by the Signora and Gabi. Then after dinner there would be a game of cards or they would dance to gramophone records while the Signora read or knitted, an unobtrusive chaperon.

Returning one evening from a stroll through the fields they were told by the elderly maidservant that a man was waiting to see them. He stood up as they came into the room, a big, well-built man of about twenty-six with dark, observant eyes and black, well-groomed hair.

'I'm Roberto Oreste,' he explained, 'and I understand you want to get into Switzerland. Maybe I can be of help.'

There was a touch of flamboyance in his speech and manner, but Paterson, who was becoming used to sizing people up quickly, immediately liked the man and felt he could be trusted.

'It's going to be a business of passing you on from contact to contact,' he explained. 'I know a Spaniard living in Milan who can put us in touch with the right people and with their help you should be able to get away. Would you like to try?'

'I think he's all right,' murmured Harris, and George nodded.

'We appreciate your help,' he told the Italian, 'and will do exactly as you say.'

A few mornings later before the first light, they left the Riccinis along with Roberto to walk three miles to the small country station where the early train for Milan made its first stop after leaving Brescia. It had been a sad farewell, with Gabi almost in tears and the two men grateful for all the kindness they had received, sorry to leave such good friends, yet somehow stimulated by the prospect of being once more on the move. Now because of the Signora's efforts, they were dressed in smart business suits, great-coats, snap-brimmed hats and comfortably fitting shoes, the kind of men to whom a Carabinieri patrolman would give an ingratiating salute.

They had no papers and feared they might have to dodge from carriage to carriage keeping out of sight of inquisitive railway police, but to their relief the journey turned out to be simple and uncomplicated.

Arriving at the station a few minutes before train time, Roberto bought the tickets. When the train rumbled in he shepherded them to a half-empty coach where they slouched down behind newspapers, completely engrossed in the day's news. The other passengers paid them not the slightest attention and the only moment of suspense came when the collector slowly worked his way down the aisle clipping tickets. If he asked a direct question would the answer in broken Italian give them away?

Now he was at the seat just behind. Sweating a little, George waited.

'Tickets, please.'

Silently they were held out while Roberto supremely confident, distracted the conductor with a string of questions. Clipping their tickets without bothering to glance at them he answered Roberto and moved on.

It was early when they pulled into Milan. Their guide piloted them through the big modern station and led them out into the streets. They struck away from the principal avenues and presently after a brisk walk, came to a quiet rather run-down district of middle-class apartments.

Roberto who obviously knew his way about, knocked at a door that was opened by a thin dark man with burning, intense eyes.

'This is Pedro, a friend of mine,' said Roberto. 'He is Spanish, but he hates Franco and will help us.'

Pedro and a plump, bleached blonde, who was explained with a wink as the girl friend, were just finishing breakfast. The young lady poured them some rather synthetic coffee.

'So you want to get to Switzerland?' asked the Spaniard pushing aside his plate and lighting a cigarette. 'Quite a few escaped prisoners have got across, but the border patrols have been increased since the Germans took over and it's getting harder. What you'll need is a guide, one of those smugglers up there who knows every path. But the difficulty will be to find them. I know a Signora here whose husband is director of a big company so she has to be discreet, but she is willing to help. She knows someone, the wife of one of her husband's employees called Maria Resta who is strongly anti-Fascist and has friends around Lake Maggiore on the border. Our idea is for this Maria to take you up to Lecco on the lake this afternoon. It's only an hour on the train. Maybe she can locate a guide. If she does, you may be safe by tomorrow.'

'Sounds a good plan,' replied George enthusiastically. 'The sooner we get away from the Gestapo and the Questura the better we'll be pleased.'

'That's settled, then,' continued Pedro, smiling a little.

'We're to meet Maria Resta this morning at the Signora's apartment to work out details. So if you've finished your coffee, we'll set off.'

The Signora, an exquisitely dressed woman of about forty-five, lived in a modern and luxurious apartment in one of the fashionable suburbs. A smartly uniformed doorman bowed them into a vestibule; a high-powered lift shot them to the eighth floor and let them out into a deep-carpeted corridor.

Inside the drawing-room a young woman plainly but neatly dressed, not pretty but nevertheless attractive because of the warmth of her smile and the friendliness of her blue-grey eyes, was waiting for them.

'This is Maria Resta,' said their hostess. 'She will do all she can to help you.'

Maria smiled a greeting. 'I have two friends, or call them acquaintances, in Lecco, and they are concerned in smuggling. I don't know where they live, but I do know the wine shops they go to and we might find them there. There is no guarantee that they would be prepared to act as guides, but I think they would because they're certainly not Fascists. If you would like to try this we can catch the two-twenty train this afternoon.'

Lecco, a clean little resort set between the lake and the mountains seemed almost dead after the bustle of Milan. 'This is the off season,' explained Maria, leading them from the station to the deserted street. She was with George, while Roberto and Harris followed twenty yards behind.

At the first wine shop they drew a blank.

'No,' answered the proprietor in response to Maria's question. 'They haven't been here in a week. No, I don't know where they could be found.'

They went on to a second, then a third, but always the answer was the same.

'No, I haven't seen them recently. They come and go and who knows where they might be now?'

The early dusk of autumn was beginning to touch the town with its greyness. Lights were coming on in stores and houses to be quickly blacked out. A Carabinieri patrolman eyed them suspiciously. They tried another tavern and another, and in each the customers stopped talking to watch and listen, but nowhere could they find the man or the information they needed.

'Could we work along the lakeshore, steal a boat and get across that way?' suggested George, prepared in his frustration to throw caution to the winds.

'No, no,' warned Maria in alarm. 'There are hundreds of guards between here and the border, and the lake is patrolled with high-speed launches. Only a good guide who knows the ground could get you through. The only sensible thing to do is to catch a train back to Milan. Some of these pigs of police are beginning to watch us. You'd better not go back to the Signora's apartment; the doorman might report you. Most of them are paid by the Questura. I will take you home. My husband is a good man, he will welcome you.'

Depressed, the high optimism of the morning gone, they journeyed back to Milan and the little three-roomed working-class apartment that was home to Maria Resta and her husband, a pleasant rather quiet young artisan who accepted his wife's strange friends without comment.

Over a late supper of spaghetti and wine they planned their next move. The food and drink quickly revived Roberto's flagging spirits and he took command of the situation.

'I have heard,' he opened a little mysteriously, 'of a man here—he's said to be wealthy—who has helped a number of prisoners escape. I don't know his name or anything about him. All I've heard is rumours. But in the morning if Maria and I go out, we might be able to find something definite and if the story is true, contact him.'

George nodded without enthusiasm. He was tired and disillusioned, cynical about fine schemes that came to nothing. He was desperate, prepared to catch at any straw. Maybe there was such a man. Maybe they could find him. Maybe he would help them.

Hell, he thought, I'd like to be somewhere where my life wasn't bounded by maybe.

The following morning Paterson and Harris waited with growing impatience in the chilly, cheaply furnished little sitting-room, half smoking and then stubbing out a chain of rank-tasting Italian cigarettes, occasionally moving to the window for a cautious look at the street below. The sky was leaden and a sad rain dripped monotonously on dirty buildings. There was no sign of Roberto and Maria.

'Do you think they've been playing us for suckers?' queried Harris suddenly, pacing anxiously back and forth. 'We'd be nicely caught just sitting here if they should turn us in for the reward. We might be smart to go back to Lecco this afternoon and try it on our own.'

'I think they're for us, Jack. They may not have proved much help, but I'm certain they're not informers. Let's wait and see. If they can't come up with something, then we'll try alone.'

Twelve o'clock struck from a neighbouring church, half past, then one o'clock. And still they waited. Suddenly there were footsteps in the corridor outside, a key turned in the lock and the door opened to admit Roberto and Maria. Both looked rather pleased with themselves.

'We've found the man,' she beamed, shaking raindrops from her brown hair.

'And we're taking you to see him this afternoon,' cut in her companion. 'He's an engineer with an office downtown. They call him Rossi though that's not his real name, but he's got a lot of people across the frontier and he's willing to help you. My friends, you're as good as out of the country.'

Signore Rossi was a small man in early middle age, well-dressed, with keen observant eyes. He smiled pleasantly as they came into his office. 'Sit down,' he said in perfect English, at the same time pushing aside a mass of papers and letters, as though to clear his desk for new business, and offered a cigarette.

Once they were settled, he addressed himself to George. 'Now, Lieutenant, tell me how you got here.'

Paterson told his story, finding it a pleasant relief to speak English again, while Rossi listened carefully, throwing in an occasional question.

'All right,' he said finally, 'I'm quite satisfied. You understand I have to be careful. The Gestapo are never far behind and I don't want to be trapped by an undercover agent. To be fair and so that we can trust each other, I'll now tell you something about myself. I am, as I think you know, an engineer by profession and my wife is English. That's why I speak the language so well. Without wishing to boast I can tell you that I've had some success in getting prisoners across the border and I have, shall we call it, the blessing of your British undercover agents in Switzerland to keep on with my work. I'm doing this for Italy because unless we get rid of these Fascists and quickly, they will drag us down to destruction. Do I make myself clear?'

George nodded. 'Very well. I can get you and your friend out of the country within several days if you want to go. But,' he paused significantly, 'I could use you in my organization if you were prepared to stay. You see,' he went on, 'when Italy surrendered there were thousands of your prisoners out on farms or doing other non-military work, and many of these took advantage of the sudden confusion before the Germans reasserted control, to disappear.

Today they are scattered throughout the countryside, hiding with families who are sympathetic, and I'm having considerable difficulty in finding and then convincing them that we are friends. This is where you could assist me. At present I have no one working in the Brescia area.' His listeners remained silent and impassive.

'This is a dangerous game as you will appreciate, but,' he continued, 'you both speak Italian and I understand that you could make your headquarters at the Riccinis where you have been staying. I don't want to rush you into this, but I could certainly use you both if you would be prepared to stay. Why not go into the other room and talk it over together?'

'What do you think?' said Harris when they were alone.

George's first reaction had been to refuse. For weeks his one objective had been to get out, to finish with this skulking and hiding, always on the run. But as he considered it his feelings changed. In the first place Rossi had deeply impressed him as an able, clear-thinking man doing a worthwhile job; secondly, in joining him he would no longer be hunted and helpless but striking back.

'I think we should stay,' he decided finally. 'He's working for our fellows and we can do something to help.'

Despite Roberto's confident assurance, George was somewhat concerned as to how they would be received on their return to the Riccinis. To shelter men for a few days was one thing, but to have them return as permanent and dangerous guests, was quite another. Yet he need not have worried. The Signora was delighted at the idea that she and her home would be actively engaged in the business of foiling the Fascists, while Gabi was delighted also, though for more personal reasons.

CHAPTER EIGHT

F o r a few days life returned to the even tenor that had existed before their trip to Milan. There were the Italian lessons with Gabi, newspapers and magazines to read, the evening walks across the fields with Harris obligingly escorting the Signora so that Gabi and he could walk together. They weren't in love—at least, he wasn't. But a mild flirtation with a pretty girl was one of the pleasanter things of life. Besides, it would be downright bad manners to remain unaffected by her obvious charm. It mustn't go too far though, he warned himself. If the Signora thought I was trifling with her daughter she might throw me to the wolves.

This middle course was not as simple as it sounded. Gabi for the first time in her life was in close association with a good-looking young man her own age and more than ready to be swept off her feet.

Fortunately, within a few days of their return Rossi's organization began to swing into action. Word would reach them that prisoners were thought to be hiding in a certain area, but sometimes there would come a definite report that an escaped British prisoner was known to be sheltering with a friendly family. Then either Jack Harris would go back with the messenger who brought them the news, or George would make the trip with Roberto who was his constant companion on these excursions. Whenever possible they used bicycles, although at times the villages were so far distant they had to use the slow local trains.

Arriving at their destination, Roberto would make discreet enquiries as to the location of the farm they were seeking, usually an isolated one a mile or so from the village. The small farmers were extremely suspicious of all strangers and Roberto would be hard put to convince them that they belonged to the resistance and not the Questura. When their good faith was finally established they would be taken to meet the guests, roughly dressed and indistinguishable from any other farm labourer.

'Hello,' he would greet them in English, 'how are you making out?'

Jaws would drop and faces register incredulous surprise. 'Gawd almighty, are you British?'

Then he would explain himself and his mission. To get them into Switzerland and eventually back to England.

'No, sir,' was the usual answer. 'We've been well treated and we help with the farm. The Eighth Army will be here in a few weeks and it would be silly for us to risk being taken at the border when all we've got to do is sit it out a little longer.'

'Unfortunately,' he would have to say, 'our armies are hundreds of miles away in the South having to fight the Germans for every inch of ground. It may be a year before they get this far, and your chances of hiding here all that time are pretty slim. If you're caught you'll be shipped into Germany and your friends will probably be shot. Believe me, Switzerland is your best bet.'

Usually the realization that they might bring disaster down upon their friends convinced the fugitives. But prying them away from their Italian hosts was another matter.

'You can't go like this. We must have a party. Tomorrow the neighbours will come and we'll get drunk and be happy.'

Resignedly George would yield to the inevitable, arranging to return two days hence to guide them to a rendezvous with one of Rossi's men who would shepherd them to Milan.

One of their expeditions led them into the foothills, behind Brescia. This time it was only a vague rumour that
Englishmen were hiding near a small village called Paldi,
but even a vague rumour had to be tracked down. He went
as usual with Roberto, cycling the first few miles into the
hills, hiding the machines in a barn and taking to the foot-
paths. They faced a ten-mile tramp over rough ground, but
the November day was crisp and clear, ideal for walking.

After an hour they struck a path leading towards their
destination and following it along, passed a couple of down-
at-heels peasants who eyed them furtively.

'*Buon giorno,*' said Roberto, getting only a surly
mumble in response.

'They're not Italian,' he whispered positively. 'I think
they're a couple of British prisoners.'

George glanced back just in time to catch one of the
men staring over his shoulder at them. Were they prisoners
or were they just a couple of yokels who might betray them
if they revealed their identity? Already they were fifty
yards away walking fast and he had to decide quickly.

'Come on,' he said, turning back. 'We'll find out.'

Roberto opened the conversation in Italian by asking
how far it was to Paldi and, even to Paterson's inex-
perienced ears, the answer they got from the taller of the
two was halting and hesitant.

'Look,' he finally broke in, speaking English. 'We know
you're P.O.W.s. So am I.'

The men were startled. Then one began to laugh.
'Jesus!' he exploded. 'Me and me mate thought you was
the bloody Questura and we was all set to clobber you. I'm
Alf Collins; used to be a driver in the Service Corps until
they nabbed me at Tobruk. Where'd you get caught?'

Collins and his mate were thoroughly enjoying their
freedom living at a nearby farmhouse where they were
treated as members of the family and solaced by the young

wives in the nearby cottages whose husbands were far away, with the army. It took more than the usual amount of persuasion to get them to abandon this Utopian existence. But at last, very reluctantly, they consented and three days later they were aboard a train for Milan en route to the border. Unfortunately the prisoners at Paldi, if they really existed, were never located, despite a long day of searching and much oblique questioning.

Several weeks later, after they had assisted twenty prisoners to freedom, they were sitting one evening in the Riccini drawing-room, playing bridge with Gabi and the Signora when there was a knock.

A knock on a door at night might mean the police. Gabi's chatter and Jack Harris's deep laugh died away as they paused to listen. A moment later the old maidservant shuffled in and behind her came a shabbily dressed young man whom George immediately recognized as one of their agents.

'I've just come back from north of Lake Garda,' he told them, pulling up a chair and bowing acknowledgement of the glass of wine the Signora poured out for him. 'I went to see my brother-in-law at Arco.'

'Hold on, hold on,' Harris interrupted. 'Signore Paterson won't understand if you don't talk slowly.'

Obviously restraining himself with difficulty the young man continued. 'There was a lot of talk in the town about a big band of partisans in the mountains that have just had a great battle with the Germans. Nobody knows what has happened, but they said there were a lot of Inglesi with them, so I thought I had better report.'

'I don't suppose you found out how many.'

The man shook his head. 'No, they don't know much in the town, but my brother-in-law has a friend who is a contact for the band. Maybe you should see him.'

George nodded, drumming his fingers on the table. 'I

guess we'd better check it out, but it's going to take several days getting there and back. Jack, you'd better stay here and look after things at this end. Roberto and I will do this one.'

The following morning with a cold wind-swept rain blowing from the water, they cycled north along the lake. This was the same road that he had staggered along in the September heat just after his escape when Luigi had found and given him shelter.

'At any rate, the Carabinieri won't bother us today,' grumbled Roberto. 'Only fools go out in weather like this.'

It was afternoon when they reached Arco and found the brother-in-law who gave them directions to the contact. Hiding their cycles in his tool shed they set off on foot.

As they climbed higher the rain ceased, but the air was colder and they came across patches of snow. Dusk was closing in and they were worried about the chance of not making it and having to spend a night out when ahead of them they saw a lodge dark against the snow.

The caretaker and his wife, a weather-beaten old couple, eyed them suspiciously but thawed when Roberto explained their role in the Resistance.

'Come in, come in,' said the old man. 'You must be hungry and cold.'

After a meal and several glasses of wine they questioned him about the partisans, the Englishmen who were with them and the battle that had been fought with the Germans. He had little knowledge.

'We don't know much except there was a fight four days ago. I'll tell you how to get there and tomorrow you can find out for yourselves. Maybe they're still there, maybe they're scattered, I don't know.'

Next day they were away early breaking trail through rough, snow-covered country that played hell with their civilian shoes. The day was bright with the uplands sparkling in the winter sun and to George it brought back sudden memories of winters at home. They climbed and descended, but the overall route was upward. After several hours they found themselves in a mountain pasture screened by belts of trees, a yellow-coloured barn to one side.

'This looks like it all right,' said Roberto, 'but the place seems deserted. We'd better scout through the woods in case it's a trap.'

They worked their way through and soon found evidence of the fight. Dead camp-fires had melted away the snow leaving circular patches of bare black ground, quantities of empty German ration tins, a helmet with a bullet hole and hundreds of empty cartridge cases. Crossing the open space towards the barn, they almost stumbled into a primitive machine-gun pit with the weapon, smashed beyond repair, pointing its barrel like a finger towards the sky. Inside the barn itself were the ashes of a dead cooking fire, but no sign of men, neither friend or foe, living, dead or wounded.

'They were captured or broke up and scattered,' suggested George.

Roberto nodded. 'Yes, I guess so. There's nothing more we can do. It's about noon, so we'll get some food and then hike back to the lodge.'

The caretaker was not so enthusiastic on their return. Possibly sober reflection and fear of the Questura had dampened his ardour, but after some argument he grudgingly allowed them to spend the night. Next morning after a breakfast of black bread they set off on the return journey.

It was dark with a drizzling rain falling when after returning their borrowed bikes they finally reached the Riccinis' gate. Suddenly they both paused, looking towards the house. Something was wrong. Different. What was it?

George felt a prickle of foreboding at the back of his neck.

'The lights in the front rooms,' he whispered, 'why aren't they on? Even if the rest of the family were out, the Signore would be home. He never goes out in the evenings.'

'Si,' agreed Roberto softly. 'Look, George,' he went on quietly after a moment's reflection, 'I'll go and find out. If it's a trap I think I can bluff them, but you'd be spotted immediately. Wait here in the bushes and see what happens.'

From a little distance he watched as Roberto knocked and waited. Several long moments passed and then suddenly the door was flung open and a man with a flashlight in one hand and what seemed like a gun in the other, confronted Roberto. He was pushed inside and the door closed ominously behind him.

George felt his stomach tighten. It was a trap and they'd got him! With an effort he fought down fear. Now he had to keep cool and watch in case there was a chance of rescue. They might send their prisoner into Brescia with only one or two guards and these might be disposed of given a little luck and a dark corner for ambush.

He waited in the darkness while the rain dripped drearily on him. The front door opened again and Roberto was pushed out. Without a backward glance he sauntered down the drive whistling cheerfully and ignoring the crouching figure of his companion. Walking out to the road he turned and headed towards town.

George waited a few moments. The door had shut and the house once again was dark and silent. Keeping in the shelter of the bushes he crept out to the lane and then ran on the grass verge to overtake Roberto.

The big Italian laughed mirthlessly as he came abreast. 'Questura all right, but I told the bloody fools that I was one of Gabi's boy friends and they believed me. They've got the Signore and Signora and God knows who else, but she's got away because they asked me if I knew where she was and who were her friends. I just acted stupid and they finally threw me out and told me to clear off.'

'I wonder what's happened to Jack.'

'Don't know. They didn't mention him. You'd better stay at my place tonight and we'll see what we can find out in the morning.'

They were out early next day, but there was little information to be had. A number of people in addition to the Riccinis had been arrested, while the remainder of their contacts among Rossi's men who had escaped the dragnet had gone to ground, the Lord knew where. As for Gabi and Jack Harris, nobody had any idea of their whereabouts.

George was depressed, blaming himself for bringing disaster on the family that had given him shelter. He must find Gabi if she was still free and try to get her to safety. But where the devil could she be? Sipping coffee in a cheap café he wrestled with the problem. Where might she have gone? Then he remembered there was a great-aunt who lived in Brescia. She had taken him once to meet her. Maybe they could find out something there.

'Come on, Roberto,' he said, gulping down his coffee, 'I've got an idea.'

The aunt was an elderly lady obviously very upset, but fortunately she remembered him.

'It's terrible,' she moaned. 'My niece in gaol like a common criminal. Gabi was here the day before yesterday. The Englishman, Jack, brought her and then went on somewhere else. He was to come back and pick her up in the evening, but before that one of the farm labourers brought us word of the arrests. We didn't know what to do. Finally Gabi decided to take the next train to Milan. She has cousins there and they will give her shelter.'

'Thank goodness for that,' breathed George. 'And what about the Englishman. Did he come back?'

The old lady nodded. 'Yes, and I told him what had happened. He said he'd better go too before they got him.'

Thanking her, they returned to Roberto's quarters to discuss their own future. 'It's not going to be possible to do much around here while the heat is on,' decided George. 'I think we'd better head for Milan and let Rossi know what's happened.'

CHAPTER NINE

Rossi sat back as they concluded their story. He looked small behind the big desk, but his eyes were keenly intelligent.

'Yes,' he nodded, 'I heard yesterday about the trouble down there, but I had no way of getting a warning to you. Thank goodness you got away safely.'

'I feel badly about the Riccinis after all they did for us,' said George.

'I honestly don't think they're in any great danger, George. Somebody informed, but Harris and you were the only evidence that could be used against them and you both got clean away. I think they'll probably be held for a while, then quietly released.'

'I hope you're right, Rossi. Now what do you want us to do? Both Roberto and I feel that Brescia is a dead issue for the moment.'

The little man nodded again. 'Yes, there'll be nothing doing for a while there, but if you want to help us we could use you in this area. There are still a lot of your men hidden in the villages on the plain and I'd like to get them out as soon as possible. Once winter really sets in it's going to be more difficult.'

George glanced at the big flamboyant Italian whom he'd come to like and admire.

'What about you, Roberto. Can you stand some more of it?'

The latter grinned broadly.

'I know a blonde up here who'll keep me from feeling lonely.'

It was arranged that Roberto would stay with some of

his friends while George moved in with an old couple who were employed as caretakers in an unused factory.

'The factory owner is sympathetic,' explained Rossi, 'and apparently the caretaker is trustworthy, so it should be a safe hideout. Here's the address, and I'll get word to you when we have a job ready.'

He stood up to end the meeting, coming round from behind the desk to shake their hands.

'Oh, by the way,' he said, looking up a little slyly at George who towered over him, 'I was in touch with a friend of yours yesterday, Gabi Riccini. She was terribly worried about you and I know that she will be delighted to hear that you're safe.'

The caretaker and his wife were a quiet but friendly couple and their cottage, adjacent to the factory yard in an industrial section of the city, looked like a safe retreat. After a simple meal George sat reading an out-of-date copy of *La Corriera Della Sera* while the old woman washed the dishes and her husband went off with lantern and keys on his evening round.

A knock at the door made him tense while the old woman shuffled across to answer. He heard a girl's voice high-pitched with excitement and an instant later Gabi was in his arms.

'Oh, George,' she sobbed, burying her head in his chest.

He stood there a little awkwardly in the middle of the room, gently patting her shoulder as she cried. The old woman, taking in the situation at a glance, quietly shut the door and left them.

'What's going to happen?' she got out between sobs. 'Thank goodness you escaped, George. Now we only have each other.'

He attempted to calm her, and as the violence of her fear and grief passed, they sat together on a battered old couch.

'Put your arms around me,' she whispered.

Hesitantly he did as she wished, and her body soft and yielding, pressed against him. His grip tightened and their lips came together. The bare poverty of the little room seemed to fade, and time stood still.

Finally, it seemed an eternity later, they were brought back to the present and reality by the murmur of the old couple's voices in the next room.

'When will we see each other again?' she whispered, still clinging to him.

'Gabi,' he said quietly, 'this is a dangerous business, as we saw down at Brescia. I could be picked up at any moment and I don't want you to become more involved.'

'I'll risk it, George.'

'I know you would, Gabi, but there's more than that. At the moment the police have no real evidence against your parents, but if they could connect you with me it would be a different matter. For their sake and for your own, we've got to say goodbye.'

There was a long pause.

'But after the war,' she faltered.

'After the war it will be a different matter, and,' he added with a smile, 'you'll have forgotten all about me by then.'

They sat together for a long while, talking a little, but mostly silent. Finally she roused herself from her thoughts.

'I must go now. My cousins will be wondering what has happened.'

'I'll see you to the tram. This is no district for a girl on her own.'

On the street corner he kissed her as they said a last goodbye and then watched, moody and depressed, as she went out of his life.

Roberto came around the following morning, his face grey and his eyes bloodshot.

'Oh, what a party,' he moaned. 'These Milanese women will be the death of me.'

'You damn lecher,' laughed George. 'Why wasn't I invited?'

Roberto had come to show him something of the city, for there would be occasions when he would have to work alone. By this time his Italian was reasonably good, thanks largely to the Riccinis, and he could get by in short simple conversations, though a more searching interrogation would quickly show him to be a foreigner.

Like a professional guide with a ready flow of patter, Roberto did the honours of Milan which he knew well. Here was La Scala, here the Piazza del Duomo, the central police station and the German Gestapo headquarters, an imposing building above which a menacing Swastika fluttered. During the day they travelled miles through the great city from the business quarter to fashionable suburbs, then across town again to workers' districts.

'Stay away from there,' joked Roberto, pointing to a vast pile of interconnected buildings surrounded by a high rampart-like wall, 'that's San Vittore, the big prison. If they get you in there, you've had it.'

From across the street George studied the foreboding structure with distaste. 'Let's get the hell out of here. It gives me the creeps. What about some food?'

They dined at an excellent restaurant patronized by well-groomed German officers and their girl friends. There were a couple at the next table and at first Paterson felt some apprehension, but the two ober-lieutenants were far too interested in their female companions to spare a thought for a couple of Italian civilians.

By God, he thought grimly, watching them covertly from the corner of his eye, it's going to be a real pleasure to win this war and take some of the swagger out of you bastards.

CHAPTER TEN

DURING the next few weeks they got a number of prisoners out, often making long train journeys to distant villages and bringing them back to Milan, but it was not so easy to find prisoners now. Many had got across the border; some had been recaptured and those that still remained had become almost indistinguishable among the peasants of the countryside. Still they and Rossi's other workers did manage to collect some, and these would be hidden in Milan and then smuggled to safety, about half a dozen at a time.

Just before Christmas they were given the job of leading several prisoners through the town to the station, where another guide waited for the short trip to Como. Roberto led the way with the others straggling behind about fifty feet apart and George bringing up the rear. The man in front of him, a short stocky lance-corporal, had just reached a street corner and was about to cross when a German scout car braked to a halt and the driver leaning out, shouted something.

Paterson edged closer expecting trouble, and caught in a flood of German the two Italian words 'via Fiamma'; apparently the driver was asking a street direction. The lance-corporal understood neither German nor Italian, but he made a shrewd guess. 'Roight deown the ruddy street, mate,' he directed with a wave of the arm, 'bear left and you cawn't miss it.'

The German smiled his appreciation, nodded thanks and drove off.

Between trips Paterson found time hanging heavily on

his hands. Even renewing acquaintance with Maria Resta and occasionally joining Roberto on one of his parties did not help. He was bored.

Fortunately at this time he met the Marino family. Marino, an industrial chemist and anti-Fascist, together with his wife and daughter Elsa, welcomed George to their home. On occasion he would escort Elsa to a movie or music hall where, to the delight of the audience and despite censorship, a considerable amount of fun was poked at the régime and its Nazi ally. Afterwards they would dine and dance, and the fact that the better restaurants were crowded with enemy officers added zest and excitement to their evenings.

'We're going to Como this weekend,' Marino told him one evening after George had brought Elsa home from a show. 'What about coming along? My mother has a villa there and she loves company. You could also be our much needed fourth at bridge.'

'I'd like to. What train are you taking? I could meet you at the station and we could all travel together.'

They left on Friday evening and in the walk from the station at Como they savoured the cold, crisp mountain air, so different from the fog and drizzle of Milan down on the plain.

It was a pleasant weekend in an easy-going family atmosphere that made the war and the underground seem very far away. The Marinos had decided to stay on and George would have liked to accept the old Signora's pressing invitation to remain with them, but Rossi had called a Monday afternoon meeting with his lieutenants to decide on future operations and he was expected. It was arranged that Elsa would travel down with him as a safety precaution. This avoided his having to buy his own ticket and, more important still, if anyone became too conversational, she could butt in and do the talking.

'We'll take the mid-morning train,' he decided. 'That will get me to town in plenty of time.'

On Monday morning they found the carriage filled largely with housewives travelling to Milan for a day's shopping, who paid no attention as they settled back in their seats.

'The one good thing about this journey is that it's short,' he whispered.

They passed through several villages, but at Monza the train ground to an unexpected halt. Surprised, he glanced up from his newspaper. On the platform waiting to board was half a company of Fascist youth, black-shirted thugs who were organized into semi-military formations.

'Identity check.' The words passed up and down the coach and women began hunting through handbags for their cards. These checks did happen occasionally and George had always dreaded being caught in one, for he had no card. This was because he felt that, should he be re-taken, he would be considered only as an escaped prisoner on the run and not as a spy with forged documents.

For an instant he was stunned by the suddenness of this approaching disaster, but there was not a moment to be lost.

'I think the game's up,' he whispered to Elsa. 'I'm going into the next carriage and remember, if I'm taken, you don't know me.'

He walked back along the train seeking desperately for an unguarded door, but already it was too late and the youths shouting, laughing, sensing their importance, small though it was, were scrambling in.

He got through to the next car and was pushing his way along the crowded aisle when a surly lout stopped him.

'Your card,' he demanded.

'I showed the man back there,' snapped George. 'Let me pass; I'm in a hurry.'

The other hesitated undecided, then grudgingly stepped back, giving way.

'Just a moment, Signore,' called a new voice and Paterson's instant of triumph vanished. He swung round to face a balding middle-aged man in civilian clothes, one of the passengers.

'I'm an officer of the Questura,' went on the man, 'and you must show your identification card.'

George was desperate and weighed his chances of breaking away, but there was no hope. Already several of the young Fascists were staring at him suspiciously. 'All right,' he admitted in angry disgust, 'I haven't got one. I'm an escaped British officer.'

If he had said that he was Winston Churchill or Josef Stalin it couldn't have created a greater sensation. It took several seconds for this to register on the Blackshirts, then with cries of 'Grab him, the English swine,' they hurled themselves on him like rugby tacklers while the women in the adjacent seats screamed and stampeded down the coach with one fat old lady leading the rush and locking herself into the men's lavatory.

The Questura agent had paled, stepped back, and after fumbling inside his coat produced a revolver half as big as himself which he waved recklessly shouting encouragement to the young men. Paterson did not struggle as there was no point in it, and they very quickly had him pinioned.

'Search him, search him,' squeaked the police agent, 'he may have a gun.'

Rough hands went through his pockets and his few possessions were piled on the seat.

'Ah, ah, what's this?' questioned the official pouncing upon something. It was a snapshot and in a sudden flash of memory George cursed his own stupidity. Just before he had left to meet the Marinos, Roberto had come round to tell him of the meeting called by Rossi and presented him with a picture of himself.

'The little blonde took it and I think it's rather good,' Roberto had said cheerfully.

He had thanked Roberto and slipped it into his pocket, meaning to hide it somewhere, for pictures could be dangerous, but in the rush he had forgotten and now he was caught with it.

'That's my brother in Canada,' he lied, and the man seemed to accept this, replacing the snapshot with the other items.

Everything was now utmost confusion, a babel of talking, shouting, gesticulating Italians.

'Clear the coach, clear the coach,' screamed the Questura agent, rushing to push out some of the more curious who were pressing in.

'Let me sit down,' growled Paterson, and as his guards made no objection, he seated himself beside his small pile of possessions. While his captors laughed and chattered he surreptitiously pushed the snapshot off the seat on to the floor, and then scuffed it out of sight. The action was unobserved and a few minutes later when a sergeant carefully gathered up the items its absence was not noticed.

There was a wait now as no one was quite certain what to do, but finally after half an hour he was literally dragged off and the train continued its delayed journey.

Surrounded by crowing Blackshirts and with the idle and curious coming along for the fun, he was paraded out of the station and down the street to the local barracks where a somewhat dirty mess-room was appropriated to accommodate the spectators who crowded in.

These young men who had grown up under Fascism, swaggering bullies completely dominated by their own propaganda, were now angry and perplexed at what the war was doing to their invincible Italy. Like all bullies they needed a scapegoat and now they had one in their power. George was reviled, spat upon and taunted, blamed for every disaster that the war had brought to them whether it was the loss of a relative or the bombing of a city.

He didn't bother to answer. Compared with the overwhelming calamity of his recapture their insults were like the buzzing of flies. He just sat still, heavy with depression, deep in his own thoughts.

His silence irritated them into an ugly, threatening mood and given the chance they would have been on him like a pack of dogs. Fortunately for him the door opened and a fleshy young lieutenant, black hair shining with oil and smelling strongly of scent, sauntered in, a voluptuous woman clinging to his arm. The soldiers drew back and the pair came close to stare at the prisoner.

'Ah, ah, my fine fellow,' laughed the officer, reaching over and pinching the captive's cheek, 'this ends the war for you.'

At the man's touch all George's self-control broke in a burst of violent rage.

'Get your dirty paws off me, you black bastard,' he stormed, starting up to swing at the man.

Almost instantly a dozen of them were on him kicking and punching. When they had him secure again the lieutenant who had hurriedly backed away from the fight, came forward and encouraged by a chorus of bravos, smashed George savagely across the face.

'Pig,' he screeched angrily, 'how do you like that, and that.'

After some more abuse the officer and his woman left and now, as though their hunger for violence had been temporarily assuaged, the others left him alone. Time passed and he wondered what was to happen to him. Then through a window he saw a car come across the barrack yard and stop outside. Two men in plain-clothes came in and the older, speaking with authority, ordered the Fascists back.

'We're from the Questura,' said one. 'You are a British officer?'

'I'm a Canadian serving with the British Army.'

'What's your name? What camp did you escape from?'

George gave the information.

'Where did you get those clothes?'

'A man gave them to me.'

'Who?'

'I can't remember.'

'You had money in your pocket. Where did you get it?'

'I can't remember.'

This went on for about an hour, with George relying almost exclusively on the words 'I can't remember'. Finally the men stood up and one produced a pair of handcuffs.

Automatically he protested being chained, but it was no use.

'I'm sorry,' said the senior man, 'I'm an officer myself, a captain of Bersaglieri and I understand your feelings, but I have my orders ... I don't blame you,' he continued, 'you are doing your duty, but those who have helped you ... Alas for poor Italy with so many traitors among her people.'

CHAPTER ELEVEN

THE early dusk of late January was closing in softening the sharp outlines of the buildings as they drove through Milan. The pavements were crowded with hurrying people, the outpourings of factory, store and office, all intent on scurrying for shelter before the approaching night, unmindful of the small black Fiat that nosed past and the handcuffed man who slumped dejectedly in the back seat. Sombrely Paterson watched them wondering when, if ever, he would again form a part of just such a hurrying, self-absorbed crowd.

'Here,' said the Questura captain not unkindly, passing him a lighted cigarette, 'you'd better have this now. Where you're going they're in short supply.'

A few minutes later they rounded a corner and then, even in the increasing darkness he knew where he was. San Vittore with its black menacing hulk crouched against the night sky awaited him in ominous silence.

They pulled in through a gate and were directed to a guardroom. A heavily built Fascist sergeant with the suspicious eyes of a gaoler signed for him like a bundle of goods and the Bersaglieri captain removed the handcuffs.

'In there,' ordered the sergeant, waving towards a small bare cubicle which had a wooden bench as its only furniture.

Paterson dropped dejectedly. Half an hour passed and then suddenly he heard the scraping of chairs, the clicking of heels and a voice snapping out an order in German. Then his own door was thrown open. A young man strode in, a big, blond, good-looking fellow with hard blue eyes that missed nothing. He wore a well-pressed sergeant-major's uniform that carried the lightning flash insignia of the S.S. on the collar. The two men eyed each other with mutual hostility.

'*Steh auf wenn ich mit dir sprech,*' barked the German, as though on a parade square.

George shook his head to indicate that he didn't understand.

This infuriated the other. His face became mottled with red and he launched into an angry tirade, while his hand went down to the revolver holster by his side. A small, meek-looking man in civilian clothes who had been standing by the door now edged forward and listened respectfully to the outburst. Then he turned to Paterson and spoke in Italian.

'Sergeant-Major Swartz says that he is the commandant of this prison and you are to get to your feet when he speaks to you.'

'Tell the Sergeant-Major that I'm an officer and in my army it's not the custom for officers to stand for sergeant-majors.'

This enraged the S.S. man even more. Once again he let loose a furious outburst, stamping his iron-shod boots in emphasis and half drawing the revolver out of its holster.

'Sergeant-Major Swartz says that he doesn't care whether you're an officer or just a common spy. Either you stand up or he will shoot you.'

George weighed the decision quickly. He knew that S.S. sergeant-majors sometimes held positions of great authority and apparently this man actually was the commandant. Why quibble? Mock heroics would certainly get him shot down in cold blood by this power-crazed enemy. Reluctantly he stood up.

Satisfied that he had asserted himself Swartz pushed the revolver back in its holster, surveyed his antagonist for a moment or two, then swung about and left the room, the little interpreter trotting at his heels. There were more shouted orders and Paterson was taken in tow by a couple of S.S. men who motioned him to come with them.

He was led from the guardroom across a gravelled courtyard and into the main building. From a central rotunda he was taken through one of a number of grilled iron doors, along a passageway and into a large four-tiered cell block. There was little time to look about before he was roughly pushed into one of the cells and the massive wooden door, bare except for a peep-hole slot, slammed and locked on him.

The luxury suite, he thought dryly, surveying the austere bleakness of the grey cement walls to which were bolted an iron bedstead and a small bench. Apart from these there was a straw mattress, one blanket, a tin wash bowl and a *buiolo* or clay chamber-pot. There were no windows but a small slot cut through the thick outer wall let in air. By craning his neck he could look upwards to see a tiny patch of black sky.

What a bloody mess, he thought disconsolately, sitting down on the bunk and pulling the blanket over his shoulders, for the place was cold. He sat there for a long time with gloomy thoughts that were only once distracted when the peep-hole cover slid back and someone glanced in. Then the metal cover slid shut with a faint click and he was on his own again. Finally he dropped into a fitful sleep, disturbed by the light from the ceiling bulb which remained on at all times.

The morning started with the rattle of keys, the banging of cell doors and the clink of crockery. He glanced at his wrist-watch which for some reason had been left him. Six o'clock. Then his own door was thrown open.

'Stay where you are,' ordered an Italian turnkey, moving on to open the next cell. A few minutes later breakfast arrived, a cup of lukewarm black ersatz coffee and a small dry roll of grey unappetizing bread. The two orderlies, prisoners themselves, slapped the items on the bench and left him.

George sat on the edge of the bunk and surveyed the meal with distaste. He wasn't hungry. A man darted in, furtive and frightened.

'I'm next door,' he whispered hurriedly. 'Are you going to eat that?'

Paterson shook his head and without another word the man grabbed up the roll and disappeared. By the next day his own growing hunger made him understand why the man would risk punishment for a chunk of bread.

Apart from this meal he was to find that lunch consisted of a bowl of watery vegetable soup and supper another cup of black ersatz coffee, a diet that would support life, but so weaken and enervate the prisoners that they would fight like dogs around a garbage can for any scrap of food.

'All right,' said the turnkey, reappearing once again, 'it's your turn. Take your *buiolo* and empty it in the latrine and get yourself water.'

The latrine was a hole cut into an underground sewer, while close beside it was a standpipe for cold water. He got a quick wash, filled his tin basin and under the guard's watchful eye, hurried back to his cell. Whereupon the door was once more slammed and locked.

This isolation continued for three days, much of which he spent restlessly pacing the floor. On the third afternoon he had visitors, two fair-haired civilians with deadpan faces.

'Gestapo,' they told him curtly in bad Italian. 'Come with us and don't try to escape—we're armed.'

With one on either side he was led through the prison out of the main gate and into the streets. After only three days of solitude combined with fear, depression and uncertainty, it came as something of a surprise that the men and women they passed were laughing and talking, without care or worry. He wondered what was going to happen to him. This would be an interrogation and he hoped to God they wouldn't decide to look upon him as a spy with the inevitable penalty.

Their destination was the Albergo Regina, infamous headquarters of the Gestapo. There was a uniformed sentinel on duty at the door. In the vestibule a number of civilians, both men and women, Germans by their speech, chatted, read, played cards or just lounged. Gestapo agents he guessed, but he was hustled on through, down a corridor and into a private room. There were two men awaiting him, and one speaking very good English told him to sit down.

'Your name, rank and religion.'

'What prisoner-of-war camps were you in?'

'How did you escape?'

All these he could and did answer, but now they moved to dangerous ground.

'Who has helped you?'

'Where did you get your clothes and money?'

'Where have you been living?'

'What have you been doing? You've been spying and sending reports to the British in Switzerland, haven't you?'

On and on it went and as the agents became tired and irritated, the threat that he might be shot as a spy occurred more frequently, but he stuck tenaciously to his story that since escaping he had wandered about the countryside getting occasional help from Italians whom he could not remember or identify. Because of the border guards he was unable to find a way into Switzerland.

Finally, not sure whether he had convinced them or not, he was dismissed and escorted back to San Vittore.

Two more days of solitary dragged by with the light

bulb in the ceiling wiping out the difference between night and day. Then he was moved to another cell already occupied by a frightened old man, who viewed him with considerable suspicion. As a Canadian he was one of the hated enemy who had brought so much misfortune to poor Italy, but the need to talk, to tell his story, at last broke down the old man's reserve.

He had spent a blameless life as a petty civil servant, going home in the evenings to his little house near Porta Cinese where he looked after an invalid and bedridden sister. Then someone, he didn't know who, had informed against him, but for what he had never been told. Without charge or trial he was arrested and had now spent three months in San Vittore under suspicion.

'What has happened to my poor sister? She was so helpless and only had me to take care of her,' he wondered despairingly.

Things were much improved as far as George was concerned. The food remained just the same and now he bolted down his share with as much eagerness as the others. However, he had the old man to talk with and they were allowed out in groups for an hour's exercise in the courtyard. Most of them were too weak for more than a slow walk up and down its length, but it gave them an opportunity to talk and exchange the *buiolo* rumours which raced through the prison. Now he was able to survey the massive defences of San Vittore which were absolutely escape-proof according to his fellow inmates.

It was built in the shape of a huge star with six separate cell blocks, four-storied buildings each capable of holding four or five hundred prisoners. Between the various rays as they were called, there were triangular-shaped courtyards each with a twelve-foot wall at its open end, and it was into these courtyards that the prisoners were allowed to go through side doors for their supervised exercise. Beyond the courtyard wall a wide gravel road encircled the prison and beyond this again was another outer wall even higher, studded with guard towers and machine-gun posts which were garrisoned by Fascist infantry.

The gaolers inside were Italian. They were the old pre-war staff and they were not particularly hostile as long as nothing was done to endanger their positions, but over them was Sergeant-Major Swartz and his assistant, Corporal Franz, with a dozen German troopers, all past-masters in the fine art of brutality.

'Watch out for Swartz and Franz especially. They're monsters,' he was warned by Don Alfredo, a mild-mannered parish priest who had made the fatal mistake of speaking against the régime.

Evidence of this was not slow in coming. One frightened prisoner who dropped a basket of dirt and floor sweepings in front of the Sergeant-Major was put to licking it up with his tongue, but the usual punishment favoured by this man was to set those who had offended him racing up and down the length of the ray on their elbows and knees. Within a few minutes the rough cement floor would wear through clothes, leaving the skin underneath torn and bloody.

George was put to work as an orderly cleaning out vacated cells and replacing lice-ridden blankets with clean ones from the store-room. This gave him daytime freedom to come and go as he pleased within the ray, always being sure to appear busy when the Germans were about and as far as possible keeping out of their way. They were all unpleasant, but Franz was by far the worst. A squat, hairy and powerful brute, he took sadistic satisfaction in using his boots on a man and his appearance on one of the floors invariably meant that some poor devil would be kicked into unconsciousness.

About this time the fourth-floor tiers of cells were

cleared of the usual run of political prisoners and a couple of hundred frightened Jews, men, women and children, were herded in, the first of many such batches collected at San Vittore for transport to the death camp at Matthausen in Austria. They were pitiful in the extreme, people without hope, knowing that they were marked to die and numbed into a sort of apathy by the thought of the approaching horror.

George and his fellow orderlies, enemies and victims of the same madness, did what they could with the gift of a piece of bread, a much-prized cigarette or a few whispered words of encouragement. It was pitifully little, yet there was no more they could do, for the Jews were constantly watched and terrorized by the Germans, especially by Corporal Franz who became more brutal than ever with these unfortunate people. Kickings and beatings were the order of the day and on one terrible morning in a fit of uncontrollable rage, he snatched a crying baby from its mother's arms, swung it against the concrete wall, then tossed the lifeless body back to the fainting woman.

For Paterson the weeks dragged by. He was always hungry, always cold, always wary, trying to keep out of the way of Swartz and Franz. Some of the prisoners received food parcels. Because he was a Canadian and far away from his own family and the hope of any packages, they were good to him and he always received a share, whether it was biscuits, candy, bread or even that most valuable of all luxuries, a few cigarettes. On one gala occasion he was given a whole packet and it seemed to him that he had never received such a splendid gift.

The idea of escape never left him. As he learnt the geography of the prison, he sought desperately for a weak point, but as far as he could see there was none. His only chance lay through locked and heavily guarded doors into the rotunda where warders were on duty day and night, or through the side door into the courtyard which was blocked by the twelve-foot wall visible from both inside the building and from the outer guard towers.

Gradually he gave up the idea of escape and concentrated on the grim struggle to keep alive and sane until that distant time when the war would be over. In this struggle small matters were important. Being able to leave his cell to use the latrine instead of having to rely on the *buiolo*, getting outside during exercise period to exchange news and talk with the other prisoners and, most important of all, the weekly visit to the women's section, taking piles of dirty blankets to the laundry—these things made life tolerable. To the prisoners, especially hot-blooded Italians deprived of all female companionship, this opportunity just to look at a woman was like spreading a feast before the hungry.

Among the thousands of prisoners in San Vittore nursing murder in their hearts towards their S.S. overlords, only Sebastiani the chef could do more than dream of revenge. He was a cheerful little man with an artist's pride in his profession and Swartz had commandeered him as his personal cook.

One day he confided in George, smiling happily.

'You know, I make sure the Sergeant-Major has something of Italy in everything he eats. I spit in every dish.'

Slowly the bitter cold of winter passed and spring brought warmth but little hope to the ray. The secret police dragged in a steady stream of suspects while some, such as the old man from the Porta Cinese against whom not even a particle of evidence was forthcoming, were released. Others found a different release. An hour before dawn a squad of S.S. their iron heels clinking on the concrete would march in. A warder would lead them to a cell usually in the isolation section, throw open the door and the condemned man would be hustled off either yelling, cursing, protesting innocence or just stoically silent, to a waiting van. There was the drive to the disused quarry, the shots and an extra cell for the orderlies to clean out.

After the old man left George was moved in with Rudi, an Austro-Italian who spoke four languages. He was a stimulating companion and the source of much accurate information, for the Germans used him as an interpreter.

'This is a tight squeeze, George,' he commented one day, 'but I think I'll soon be moving out.'

'Have you got a release?'

'Not that kind,' he answered with a bitter laugh. 'I'm quarter Jewish, and Swartz knows it. As soon as he finds a replacement for me I'll be on my way to Matthausen.'

Six weeks later the prophecy was fulfilled.

CHAPTER TWELVE

ONE afternoon in early June, Paterson was distributing a load of clean blankets when coming out of a door he almost ran into a couple of Germans. Stepping hurriedly aside, he nearly dropped the load in shocked surprise.

Between the two burly soldiers was a small, slightly built man who was roughly hustled into the nearest isolation cell. He knew the man. It was Rossi.

This was a nasty shock. The whole organization depended upon him for leadership, and without him it would quickly fall to pieces. While Rossi was on the outside there was always the hope that they might come up with some plan to get him out. Now that hope was gone. He must find a way to speak to him, but that would be utterly impossible while he was in isolation. The only thing to do was to watch and wait.

Next morning he made pretence of sweeping near the cell. Promptly at ten o'clock two plain-clothes Gestapo men arrived, and Rossi, rumpled and unshaven, was whisked off between them.

The hours went by. It was nearly four o'clock before they brought him back, white and drawn, and pushed him into the cell.

If they haven't managed to pin anything on him he'll probably be put in with the rest of us tomorrow, speculated George. Next day the Gestapo returned to hustle Rossi off for more long hours of questioning and with each day George's concern for his friend increased. This was no routine examination. They must know that they had caught a very big fish.

The isolation punctuated by interviews went on relentlessly for days. Then suddenly when Paterson had pretty well given up all hope it ceased, and Rossi appeared with the other prisoners and, by good luck, was set to work in the same gang of orderlies as George.

They managed to sneak a few minutes in an empty cell. 'What the hell happened?' George asked, not wasting time on useless greetings.

Rossi shrugged.

'The luck was not with me. What you call a tough break.'

They heard a warder's step outside and he fell silent for a moment while the man passed, then continued. 'I had to make up a report for your people in Switzerland on the number of men that we had got out. Nearly three thousand,' he added with a touch of pride, 'and it was in my pocket when the Gestapo picked me up. I've found out since that they didn't have a damn thing on me. Some kind friend had denounced me, but without a shadow of evidence to back it up. Then when they got their hands on that paper the fat was really in the fire. Still, the swine didn't get anything useful out of me for all their questioning.' He looked tired and suddenly old, but his voice held hard defiance.

The younger man nodded sympathetically.

'I figured you were getting a rough time. What happens now?'

'I'm waiting court-martial. That means either shooting or life imprisonment and I've got a feeling that I'm slated for the firing squad.'

'They don't waste much time on formalities. We've got to do something quickly, but I'm damned if I know what. This place is said to be escape-proof and I haven't been able to figure a way out.'

Rossi's voice dropped to a whisper.

'Listen, George, there's always a way out if you have money. It's costing plenty, but I've got one of the turnkeys bribed and he's planning an escape for us. There's you and me, and I want to take out three other men who worked for me.' He mentioned the names and George knew them, but not that they had been in the same organization. 'It's not final yet,' continued the Italian, 'but as soon as it is I'll give you the details. If things go right we may be away in a week. Now we'd better separate before Franz comes sniffing around. I'm not exactly popular with those gentlemen.'

Five days of growing excitement and nervous tension passed before Rossi again spoke to him. This time it was during the exercise period. 'Come over here, George, we won't be noticed in the crowd.'

Leaning casually against the wall the little man spoke quietly.

'Have you still got your civilian clothes?'

'Yes, in my cell.'

'Good! Well, here's what we're going to do.'

The plan was based on a thorough knowledge of the workings of the prison and its staff. Each ray had two doors, one on either side leading out to the adjoining courtyard. The courtyard on the far side of the next ray had a gate, open and unguarded, that was used by trucks bringing in supplies to the store-rooms. In the mid-summer heat of the early afternoon when the inside staff and the soldiers on duty at the outer wall had finished their heavy mid-day meal, there was a period of siesta when almost everybody, including the prisoners, was drowsy and lethargic. Even the duty warders managed to find a bench near their post for a cat-nap. This was the time chosen for the break and they were to follow each other at ten-minute intervals, wearing civilian clothes under the prison overalls.

'Luckily all five of us are orderlies,' went on Rossi, 'so if we each carry blankets it will look as if we are on duty. I'll go first at two-thirty, and you'll leave the cell block sharp at twenty-to-three. Cross this exercise yard, walk right through the next ray dropping your blankets in a corner somewhere, then through the far side door and out into the next courtyard where the gate is kept open during the day. Have you got that?'

The Canadian nodded.

'Good. Once you get through the gate you're between the two walls. About fifty yards along to the right there's a shed built against the outer wall where they store shovels and wheelbarrows. If any of the sentries notice you they'll think you've been sent to get one. Inside the shed strip off your overalls and hide them somewhere. Got that? Now just beyond there's a small postern door in the wall that's always kept locked but isn't guarded. The warder I've bribed has managed to get a wax impression of the key and he's getting a duplicate made up. I'll unlock the door so that you others can follow easily. Don't forget to shut it after you. Once you're in the street get away fast and hide.'

Paterson nodded again. 'When do we go?'

'My man will try the key this evening and if it fits we'll go tomorrow. If there's any hitch we'll have to put it off a day. I'll let you know definitely in the morning.'

For the rest of that day and most of the night George was in a fever of impatience, his mood varying from wild exhilaration at the prospect of imminent freedom to the depths of despondency in the certainty that at the last moment something would go wrong. Their man might betray them or fail to turn up with the key. An alert sentry might stop them. There seemed no end to the possible mischances. Next morning as soon as he could he was out of his cell watching for Rossi who was now working with another gang. It was mid-morning before their paths crossed, both with arms full of dirty blankets.

'The shoe didn't fit,' whispered the little man tersely. 'It's gone back to the shoemaker.'

Blast, George thought, another twenty-four hours.

For months he had steeled himself to endure the nightmare of prison life, but now with freedom so tantalizingly near, the disappointment of even one added day was a calamity. The following morning Rossi again shook his head.

'Damn thing still won't turn. It's gone back to be refiled.'

The third morning he smiled and nodded. 'This afternoon,' he whispered hurriedly as Corporal Franz hove into view. 'Remember you're at twenty-to-three.'

Somehow the day ground on until finally they were dismissed to their cells for the mid-day soup. Outside, the July sun was glaring down on the land like an angry eye, while even in the concrete depths of the rays, the heat was heavy and oppressive, full of the smells of prison, disinfectant, boiled cabbage and urine. It was the quiet period when, except for a few orderlies on special duty, no one stirred.

For the thousandth time he ran over the plan, rechecked his civilian clothing on a peg in the corner and the pile of dirty blankets that he had thrown out of sight behind the door. He glanced at his watch. Twenty-five-to-two. More than an hour yet.

Restlessly he began pacing back and forth. No, he shouldn't do that, it might attract attention if a warder should pass. He sat down, every nerve tingling for action, and lighted a carefully saved cigarette butt.

For what seemed an eternity he forced himself to relax and not look at his watch until in sudden panic—perhaps he had let it go too long—he glanced at the dial. Ten after two. In a few minutes he would get into his clothes, but he didn't want to do it too soon. Under the overalls sweat trickled down his ribs while his breathing became harsh and irregular as the strain increased.

By half past he was ready. Rossi would be leaving now, mentally he followed him step by step, minute by minute waiting for the yell of alarm or the shot but nothing disturbed the heavy silence. Two more minutes; then it would be his turn. Now every second was an eternity. The breathless moments crept past and suddenly the minute hand was dead on eight. Time to go.

Scooping up the blankets, forcing himself to keep a slow and deliberate pace, George walked out from the cell glancing to right and left. By the exit to the rotunda a turnkey, his tunic unbuttoned to show a dirty, sweat-stained shirt, dozed on a bench. Down at the far end he could see two more, one asleep, the other reading a newspaper. None stirred or looked up as he walked down the line of cells. Then he turned into the side corridor, momentarily out of sight. Now he had to cross the exercise yard where he would be visible from windows in the rotunda.

The light was dazzling as he stepped outside and the air was heavy with heat. He felt there were eyes on him and his legs were rubbery but no challenge was shouted. There was no sound save for his footsteps on the hard-packed ground. It was only a matter of thirty yards across but it seemed like an eternity out in the open before he reached the door and slipped into the gloom of the adjoining ray. A guard slouched on a chair smoking and reading a magazine. He looked up and their eyes met. For a terrible moment George thought he was going to be called over and questioned. Apparently, however, the pile of blankets satisfied the guard who turned back to his reading.

His pulse racing, he covered the last few paces into the corridor and once out of view hastily dropped the blankets in a corner by one of the latrines and slipped out through the side door into the next courtyard. There was a prison truck parked by a small loading ramp on the far side, but no one was about and there in the courtyard wall stood the open gate that Rossi had promised. Once again he forced himself to a deliberate pace. He had the feeling that eyes were watching him from the rotunda windows and he tensed ready to run at the first shout, but nothing interrupted the mid-afternoon quiet. Now he was at the gate and out into the gravel roadway between the two walls. Fifty yards to the right was the lean-to shed. If only he could cover that last piece of ground unobserved. A quick glance upward showed the heads of a couple of sentries on the outer wall. They paid no attention.

Twenty paces. Ten. Five. Then he bolted through the half-open door into the blessed shelter of the lean-to. It was dark inside, but he could see rakes, shovels and several wheelbarrows.

With fingers fumbling from sweat and nervousness he wrestled with the overall buttons and finally stripped the garment off. Smoothing out the fedora which he had carried crumpled under his arm he glanced out. Not a soul in sight, and the door to freedom just around the corner of the shed.

A momentary hesitation gripped him. Miraculously he had got this far. A challenge from the wall, the sudden appearance of a warder and his dream would collapse. Here in the half-darkness he was hidden, safe for the moment.

Stop being a bloody fool, he told himself and get moving.

A few steps took him round the corner. Ahead the postern door was shut but unguarded. He turned the handle and pulled, half expecting to find that his good luck had run out and for some unaccountable reason it was locked. It swung open and in an instant he was through, quietly pulling it closed behind him.

Incredibly he was free. For an instant he stood sensing the wonder of it. Then he remembered the warning, 'Get away quickly.'

The prison wall stretched away on either side and out in the road there were some tracks. In the distance he could hear a tram rattling its slow way towards him. That was the answer. He turned and walked along the empty sidewalk towards the corner, keeping well in to the wall to avoid being noticed by the sentries above.

The worry, the tension was over. Somehow they had done the impossible and got out of San Vittore. He felt lightheaded with relief and triumph. They'd shown the bastards!

At that moment a figure came round the corner fifty yards ahead. A burly figure dressed in the green-grey uniform of the S.S. George started and suddenly felt sick. It was one of Corporal Franz's henchmen, a lumbering thug of a fellow who had more than once made his life a misery. Desperately he fought down the panic that gripped his mind. What the hell should he do?

The distance between them was closing fast. If he turned now and walked away the man would be suspicious. He might call on him to halt and then recognition would be certain, but if he tried to run for it the soldiers on the wall above would riddle him with their fire. The only thing was to keep on and hope to God to pass unnoticed. Heinrich, that was the man's name, would not be expecting to meet a prisoner in civilian clothes outside the wall.

Pulling the brim of his hat down he walked on looking straight ahead. For an instant Heinrich's eyes flickered in his direction, but it was only the most casual of glances; then, not deigning any further interest in a mere Italian civilian, he was past.

Resisting the strong temptation to glance back, Paterson walked to the corner and waited, ignoring the watch-tower that rose up behind him, though he could almost feel the eyes of the guards boring into his back. With maddening slowness the tram ambled its way along, and halted to let him board it. The bell clanged and it jerked into motion. By the time he had bought a ticket and got a seat, the menacing grey mass of San Vittore had almost disappeared behind a wall of factories and warehouses.

CHAPTER THIRTEEN

'GIORGIO, Giorgio, it's so good to see you,' cried Maria throwing her arms about him. 'We thought you were in prison.'

'I was,' he grinned, disentangling himself, 'but I've just got out. Can you hide me?'

'Of course, but tell me all about it.' She pushed him into a chair, poured wine and passed him a cigarette. 'Now, let's hear everything.'

He was exhausted physically and mentally, but the wine and her genuine happiness at seeing him again carried him along. Halfway through the story Fortunato, Maria's husband, returned from work and he had to begin again talking and eating and drinking until late in the evening. He was more than a little tipsy by the time he got to bed, draping his long form uncomfortably over the chesterfield while his stomach, so used to the near starvation diet of prison, rebelled against the generous portions of spaghetti, cheese and fruit which he had eaten. It was a bad night, turning fitfully from one awkward position to another while every detail of the escape went through his mind again and again. How had the others got on? Were the Gestapo and the Questura combing Milan in a giant man-hunt?

Morning found him disturbed—starting at every noise. A car drew up in the street below and he ran to the window to peer down from behind the curtain. Thank God it wasn't the police.

'Sit down, Giorgio, you're safe here,' Maria assured him, but he couldn't relax. Every noise in the corridor made him start; every sound from the street had him peering down from behind the curtain.

'My nerves are on edge,' he confessed, 'and the thought of being dragged back to that hell-hole gives me the jitters.'

In the afternoon Maria went out to do her shopping. Rossi had given him a phone number where he could be contacted if they made it and Paterson gave this to her.

'See what he's going to do and what his advice is,' he told her.

He spent a miserable and restless hour on his own, but her smile when she returned reassured him.

'Rossi said that everyone made it.'

'Good,' grunted George.

'He thinks there's no hope of doing anything here at present. He's going to Switzerland while the heat is on and advises you to go there too. He's given me the number of a fireman called Orlando, who should be able to get you across the border.'

He pondered this information for a few moments. If Rossi was going, there would be nothing left for him to do here, and besides he admitted to himself, in the shaky state he was in at present he wouldn't be much help to anybody. The best thing he could do would be to get into Switzerland and have a good rest. Then with any luck, the British might be able to smuggle him out across the South of France and back to England where he could rejoin his unit. He had heard rumours in prison, now confirmed, that the Second Front had begun a month ago and he longed for the order and security of a fighting regiment.

'Maria,' he said, 'would you be a darling and contact this man Orlando? Tell him I want to go as soon as possible.'

The fireman seemed a capable organizer. He would arrange everything and get George out of Milan as a member of the fire department. They would have to get a small passport picture though, for a forged identity card.

'He's given me the name of a photographer who can be trusted,' Maria explained. 'We could go now if you like. I've got time before Fortunato gets home.'

He was reluctant to go out into the streets with the feeling that every eye would be on him and hostile, but it had to be done if he wanted to get away and Maria would be with him. A man and woman walking together were less suspicious than a man on his own.

'Okay,' he agreed, 'we may as well get it done.'

No one seemed to pay the slightest attention during their walk through the crowded streets, but despite this he was uneasy, tensed for the arresting hand on his arm and the demand, 'This is the Questura. What's your name?'

They found a small photographer's shop on a crowded side street with its windows filled with stiffly posed family groups. The photographer was a fat, merry little man who insisted on their taking a glass of wine with him before getting down to business.

'I know Signore Orlando well,' he assured them, 'and I'll see he has the photos by tomorrow.'

After this there was nothing to do but wait as patiently as he could in Maria's apartment. All next day he hung about, afraid to go outside, unable to settle down to read. Instead he passed the time smoking, pacing back and forth and watching, carefully screened by the curtain, the activity in the street below. In the afternoon he sent Maria out to phone Orlando.

'You're going tomorrow,' she told him on her return. 'He'll take you to Como, and there's a man he's contacted there who will see you across the border. We meet him tomorrow at noon at one of the sub-stations. I know where it is.'

The day was hot, the pavement hot, and his mouth dry as they approached the fire-hall and paused before the big open doors to survey the line of shiny trucks.

What do we do now, he wondered.

A man in uniform came out from behind one of the engines. 'Signora Resta?' he enquired quietly.

'Si.'

'I'm Orlando. I'll take care of your friend.'

George turned to Maria to say goodbye with a sudden feeling of regret. He was fond of this attractive young woman who was willing to risk her freedom and safety for the things in which she believed. She was like a sister on whose absolute loyalty you could count and he would have liked to take her in his arms to give her a farewell kiss, but there were too many passers-by for any display of emotion.

'Goodbye, Maria,' he said, shaking hands, 'and thank you for everything. I'll come back after the war to see you and Fortunato.'

Turning quickly he followed the fireman past the engines and into a small room at the back.

'Here,' said the man when the door was shut, passing him a uniform jacket, trousers, boots and helmet. 'Get into these as quickly as you can.'

While George changed he explained the plan.

'Another fireman and I are driving up this afternoon to return a pump to the Como Brigade and you'll come along in the back of the van. Oh, by the way, here's your identity card, though it's very unlikely that we'll be stopped. About a mile out of Como you're to meet the guide and change back into your own clothes at his house. We'll go there first. This guide is a smuggler, so he'll know how to get you across without any trouble.'

It all sounded very simple, almost too easy.

'What about you, Orlando?' he questioned. 'Will anyone here get you into trouble for this?'

The other smiled and shook his head. 'No. Everyone on this shift is an anti-Fascist. Don't worry about me.'

He was left to wait uneasily for about half an hour, acutely aware of voices and passing footsteps from the big garage beyond, but no one came to disturb or question him. Then Orlando returned, grinning cheerfully.

'We've got the pump loaded. Are you all set to go?'

He was led to the far end of the garage where a small red Fiat van with 'Milan Fire Department' painted in black on its door panels, waited. He got in through the back while Orlando and another man settled themselves in the front seats, and then they were off, slipping quietly through the city traffic.

The trip north was uneventful. A cooling breeze came in through the open window and for the first time in weeks George began to loosen up. At last he was really on his way leaving Swartz and Franz and what they stood for far behind. He stretched out comfortably, savouring the full pleasure of relaxation.

On the outskirts of Como they swung left along a country road. In less than a mile they came to a small farmhouse half hidden among the vines that covered the lower slope of the hill.

'Wait,' ordered Orlando, getting out, 'and I'll see if everything is all right.'

He was back in a few minutes.

'Come on,' he said, 'and don't forget your clothes.'

He crawled out through the back and they walked up to the house. There were a number of people there who eyed him curiously, the farmer and his wife, several small children and a black-haired swashbuckling young man who was introduced as Francesco the guide.

'He's the greatest rascal unhung,' commented Orlando cheerfully, 'but he knows the country and he'll see you through. Now if you would like to get changed I'll get away. We don't want to keep the van parked outside too long.'

After he had gone Francesco poured wine and offered George a cigarette.

'It's too early to start yet,' he explained. 'In this business you have to know just when.'

He was a talkative flamboyant type and from the conversation George quickly surmised that he had been a part of the Rossi organization, not so much, he guessed, from any deep political conviction but merely for the pleasure of outwitting the authorities. His real occupation was smuggling and he boasted of having made enough to keep him for the rest of his life.

When the afternoon's heat was beginning to mellow he drained his glass and stood up.

'All right, Signore. If you're ready we can go.'

Climbing the slope behind the house they soon left the vineyards behind and came out on to the open hill, rough jagged moorland covered with shrubs and coarse grass and an occasional clump of trees. As casually as though he were out for a stroll in the town, Francesco led him along a path that wound across the high ground. Occasionally they would catch a glimpse of the lake below looking blue and cool in its frame of mountains and with small boats crossing its surface like water-beetles on a pond. The hill itself appeared to be theirs, without another soul in sight, though from somewhere beyond a belt of trees he did catch the tinkle of goat bells.

After an hour's walking they topped a gentle ridge and a few minutes later Francesco halted on top of a small bush-covered bluff.

'We'll wait here until the patrol goes by,' he said, dropping to the ground. George followed and the man pulled back a branch to give them a field of view.

'Do you see the path just down there?' he went on.

'That's the way they come. They're due in about ten minutes. After they pass you've got half an hour before they return. Look down the slope now. Do you see that fence?'

Paterson shaded his eyes and studied the high wire fence that ran across the flank of the hill about two hundred yards away.

'That's the border. The bottom wire is very loose, so you can easily slip under, but don't stop once you're on the other side. The Germans have a habit of shooting across if they're suspicious, so keep on going until you're out of range.'

The Canadian nodded and both men settled to wait. They didn't have long before the sound of voices and the metallic chink of equipment told them the patrol was on its way. A few minutes more and they came in sight, six Germans in the familiar green-grey field uniform, their faces red and shiny from sweat and the exertion of the climb.

George studied them from his hiding-place. They were talking and laughing, obviously concerned with nothing but making their round and getting off duty. With a smile he thought of the surprise and commotion that would be created if he tossed a pebble down among them.

Very quickly they crossed in front and disappeared from sight, but their voices kept drifting back for what seemed an endless time. Finally the hillside was silent again except for the heavy midsummer hum of insects and the rather plaintive call of an unseen bird.

'Okay,' said Francesco, sitting up. 'Now's your time. Remember, go under the wire and keep on moving once you're on the other side.'

With a hurried word of thanks Paterson slid down the bank, crossed the footpath the Germans had used a few minutes before and strode towards the border feeling as vulnerable and naked as though he were in a busy street without his clothes. Should he run for it or walk, hoping to give the impression of a peaceful citizen out for an afternoon stroll? He compromised on something between a slow run and a very fast walk.

The fence came closer and he glanced back. No sign of Francesco. No sign of anyone.

Sure enough the bottom wire was slack. He dropped to the ground and holding it up wriggled under. Then he was on his feet again and this time he ran hard bearing over to the right away from the patrol towards a small wood. Once he reached its shelter he slowed down to a walk, gasping for breath. What lousy condition I'm in, he thought.

There was a path winding through the trees and he followed it mechanically while he tried to cope with the intoxicating realization that for the first time in three and a half years he was really at liberty, not a fugitive on the run but a free man in a free country.

The trail led round a big outcrop of rock and skirting it he suddenly froze, paralysed in mind and body by what he saw. There on the path not fifty yards ahead and coming towards him fast, for they had seen him at the same instant, was a squad of soldiers in green-grey uniforms.

CHAPTER FOURTEEN

AFTER the first instant of stunned horror his immediate reaction was that by some terrible mischance he had accidentally recrossed the border into Italy. Yet that seemed impossible. The border was clearly marked by the high fence which stretched all along the Swiss frontier. Another idea followed closely. Had Francesco betrayed him? The man had seemed straightforward, but who could tell when blood money could be so easily earned.

He looked more closely at the soldiers and suddenly the fear lifted giving place to relief. The uniforms were green-grey but they weren't German.

'Are you Swiss?' he called in Italian to the leading man.

'Yes, who are you?'

'I'm a Canadian officer and I've just escaped.'

The soldiers gathered about him smiling and obviously friendly, but not particularly surprised for many others had crossed in this way. One gave him a cigarette and he drew in the comforting smoke gratefully. They had given him a bad fright and he needed a few minutes to steady himself.

'You'll have to come with us down to the guard-house,' said their spokesman, 'and see the sergeant. It's not very far.'

Their way led down through the wood and then a few hundred yards along a country lane to a red-brick guard-house. From a cottage just across the road a pleasant middle-aged woman, seeing him arrive, came across bringing a bowl of milk, no doubt hoping to hear his story in return.

His mouth was dry and he gratefully gulped down the drink between questions. There were about ten soldiers at the post, all of them friendly and quite informal.

'Are you hungry?' one asked.

He nodded. All he'd had that day was a cup of coffee at breakfast. Fresh bread, cheese and cold meat with some wine to wash it down tasted delicious.

'I'll report you to my captain at Bellinzona,' said the sergeant, an older man with a weather-beaten face, when the meal was finished. He crossed over to the field telephone in the corner and talked for some time.

'You're to stay here for the night,' he told the Canadian after ringing off, 'and they'll send a car for you in the morning.'

After a good night's sleep he felt on top of the world. The officer who questioned him in Bellinzona was more like a host than an interrogator.

'We have as our guests many of your people who have escaped,' he said in passable English, 'and I hope you will enjoy your stay. All the British and Americans go to Montreux on Lake Geneva and it is very pleasant there. First though, you must go to the quarantine centre at Bad Lostorf. I'm afraid you'll find it rather dull but comfortable,' he added with a smile, 'and it's only for a couple of weeks. Then you'll be sent on to Montreux.'

That afternoon he was put aboard a train for Bad Lostorf. The journey took three hours, with a soldier attending more as a guide than guard. The quarantine centre had been a small hotel and in the lounge a handful of American officers who had come in the previous day made him welcome.

'You're just in time for chow, soldier,' said a tall, thin young man called Harry.

They were the crew of a Liberator that had crashed just across the border in occupied France. All but the pilot and

131

Harry, had made it across without trouble, but these two had been picked up by a German frontier patrol and sent off under guard. On the way they had killed their captor and started towards the border, they hadn't got very far before the alarm was out and they had spent a long, hot nerve-racking day hiding in a wheat-field.

'It wasn't until after we'd killed him that I realized just what would happen to us if we were recaptured,' Harry said, 'and then I really began to sweat blood. Believe me that day in the wheat-field was the longest I've ever spent. Some of the Krauts walked right through it, but thank God they didn't spot us. Then when it was dark and they'd given up, we hightailed it out of there for Switzerland.'

At dinner they were served by Allied other ranks who were also going through the centre. Towards the end of the meal a new man came in from the kitchen with a tray of desserts. Seeing George, he started.

'Blimey, it's Mr. Paterson.'

Recognition was mutual.

'Well, I'll be damned. It's Jack Watson.'

His mind flashed back three and a half years to the night they had jumped into Italy, with Corporal Watson as second-in-command of his section.

'When did you get out?'

'It's a long story, sir, and I've got a jug of vino in my room. How about coming up for a drink?'

'That's an offer I can't refuse,' grinned George, excusing himself from his American friends.

Watson's story was similar to that of hundreds of others. He had got away when discipline had collapsed in the P.O.W. camps just after Mussolini's fall. From that time until he had crossed the border a week ago he had lived on a farm as a member of the family.

'When I heard about the Second Front I thought it was

time to get moving,' he explained. 'It sure would be nice to get back to England and see my old lady.'

Life at the quarantine centre was certainly relaxing. And a little dull. He was medically checked, given a crew-cut and had his clothes treated against lice, but apart from that there was little to do but eat, talk, sleep and read some of the English books in the small library. The Americans were a casual, easy-going group who left the States six months before, so they were able to bring him up to date on conditions in the outside world.

During his stay he did have an international problem. One morning the Commandant, a German-speaking Swiss captain, called him to his office and in halting Italian asked for his help.

'We have two Hindu soldiers here. They came in yesterday. Something has made them very upset, but I can't understand what. Would you try to find out?'

The men were summoned, a tall, aristocratic-looking corporal who spoke Urdu, and his companion who knew very little English. Slowly from Urdu into English and from English into Italian the story came out. Their religion demanded that they prepare their own food in cooking pots unused by others. Could this be arranged?

'Why, of course,' agreed the relieved Commandant, 'I'll give the order right away.'

After ten days George was cleared and put aboard a train for Montreux, a journey that took him through breath-takingly lovely countryside but was otherwise uneventful.

This could not have been said for the same journey taken by another lieutenant who had escaped several months previously. On the train sitting beside the young man was a very charming girl whose conversation made the trip pass all too quickly. At their destination he was summoning up nerve to ask her for a date when she staggered him by offering casually, 'Would you like me to spend the night with you?'

Being a gentleman, not wishing to slight a lady, especially one so pretty, he immediately accepted and they registered at a hotel.

Next morning she again surprised him by rising very early and getting washed and dressed, ready to leave.

'But, darling,' he protested, 'this looks like the beginning of a beautiful friendship. Do you really have to go?'

'But I must,' she replied. 'It's my wedding day and I've got to get ready.'

'But ... but ... but ...' he faltered.

Her smile was warm and kindly. 'You looked so lonely on the train and I knew you'd been a prisoner and hadn't seen any girls for a long time so I thought it was a good idea.'

Arriving at Montreux late in the afternoon George was directed to the British Administration Office. Most of the former luxury hotels perched high up behind the town and looking out across the blue waters of Lake Geneva had been taken over by the Allies. Both the British and the Americans had offices down in the town where they handled their own administration, issued pay, worked with civic officials and organized military police to keep their own men out of trouble. They had had word of his coming and the formalities were quickly completed.

'We're putting you in the Hotel Francaise,' the adjutant told him. 'They've got a first-class chef and you'll live like a fighting-cock. Now here's some money for you, three hundred francs to get yourself some clothes and another hundred to hold you till payday. Oh, by the way, the provost-marshal wants to see you. His room is just down the corridor.'

A little puzzled, he knocked and entered. A man whose

face was vaguely familiar looked up and then, grinning broadly, came forward to shake hands.

'George, it's good to see you. Don't you remember me, Jock Easton?'

'Why, of course.' He had found Jock last autumn, hiding in a foothill village and had helped him escape.

'I was afraid you had left it too long and been re-captured by the Tedeschi,' went on the other.

'I was, but it's a hell of a long story. Tell me, what's the drill around here?'

The other man briefed him on conditions.

'What I need is a party,' decided George. 'How about coming out and doing the town?'

Jock laughed. 'I thought that's what you'd want. Everyone does, but I'm all tied up tonight. What I will do is send my sergeant along to tail you and see that you get back safely. He's a good lad and he'll keep you out of trouble. Then you can come back here and sleep it off. There's a bed in the next room and I won't be using it tonight.'

It was quite a party, though unfortunately his memory of it when he awoke late the next morning was somewhat vague. He recollected dining rather well at a fashionable restaurant; moving from there to a bar; on to a night-club where he bought champagne for all the hostesses and from there to another where somehow he ended up as drummer in the band. Beyond that his mind was a blank.

The sergeant, his shadow of the previous night, must have heard him wake, for he came in from the outer office.

'Good morning, sir, and how are you this morning?'

'Good morning, Sergeant. Did I enjoy myself?'

'You certainly did, sir,' grinned the other. 'Really did it up proper.'

'Have I got any money left?'

'Not a sou,' replied the cheerful voice. 'You spent all you

135

had, borrowed a hundred from me and you still owe the last place fifty francs.'

Paterson groaned.

Later in the day, baled out financially by Jock Easton, he went to the Hotel Francaise to consider his position. It was two weeks to payday and all he had was a handful of borrowed money so there would be no more night-clubbing for a while. The best and cheapest thing would be to spend his days on the beach relaxing and soaking up sunshine. Healthy too, he assured himself half-heartedly.

The next afternoon found him on the Montreux beach, intermittently swimming and sunbathing. It was a lovely midsummer afternoon and the heat on his skin gave an almost sensuous pleasure.

Voices roused him and he looked up. A couple were spreading towels just a few yards away. The girl was tall and slim, with blue eyes and blonde hair, gorgeous in a trim white bathing suit. Fascinated, he stared at her.

Her companion, a man, saying something in English, drew his attention. He was a dark-haired young fellow, probably another escapee. Studying him somewhat resent-fully he suddenly realized that he knew him. He was one of those they had hidden in Maria Resta's flat until they made the arrangements to get them across the border. Decent chap, he remembered, but what was his name? Charlie something. Ah, now he had it—Charles Gray, that was it.

Feeling a little self-conscious he called out, 'Charles, Charles Gray.'

The other looked up quickly and stared ... Suddenly it registered ... 'Good Lord, it's George Paterson. When did you arrive?'

He came across to shake hands and introduced the girl as Karen. She spoke English with a charming trace of a French accent.

Young Gray was a voluble talker who felt a debt of grati-
tude to Paterson for getting him out of Italy so he carried
the conversation, dwelling on George's exploits in both
length and detail.

A little embarrassed by this praise his subject glanced at
the girl who was listening wide-eyed, and as he studied her,
confirming his first opinion, she turned her head slightly
and their glances met. It was only for an instant before she
turned away blushing slightly, but even that instant had
been enough to start his heart pounding. Never in his life,
he was sure, had he seen such a beautiful creature.

After a time they went swimming together in the cold
lake water and she seemed as gracefully perfect here as on
the beach. They lay on the sand to dry out and when her
first shyness was over she talked vivaciously.

'I should speak good English,' she laughed in response to
his comment. 'My father is Swiss, but Mummy's from
Bristol and we always speak it together.'

Later in the afternoon they strolled up to one of the outdoor cafés that overlooked the lake and lazily watched the
passers-by.

'What about meeting again tomorrow?' suggested
Charles. 'Same place, same time.'

George turned to Karen. 'What about you?'

She smiled. 'That would be nice. About three o'clock.'

In the days that followed Charles, chagrined but with
rare tact, faded out of the picture, leaving them alone.
There was a mutual affinity between George and Karen.
Both enjoyed the same things, swimming, hiking, dancing
or cycling along the lakeshore to some picturesque beauty
spot, almost deserted now that tourists no longer came to
Switzerland. They were completely happy. The hours he
spent with Karen, golden sun-filled hours, made every
moment away from her drab and colourless and each
meeting a shining new adventure. For the first time in

years he almost forgot the war, but it had not forgotten him.

He was having lunch in the hotel one day some weeks later before meeting Karen for their afternoon swim, when the Adjutant came over.

'George,' he said, 'I got a message in this morning for you. You're to go up to Berne tomorrow and see a Mr. McTavish in the British Press Office. God knows what they want with you, but that's the order. Here's some money for your ticket and meals. Right?'

He was puzzled by the invitation. If he had had any journalistic experience they might have been offering him a job, but school essays and terse military reports were the sum total of his literary output.

'I'll go up and see what they have on their minds,' he promised.

A taxi took him from the station at Berne to the British Press Office the following morning.

'Yes, Mr. McTavish is expecting you,' an attractive receptionist told him. 'Will you come this way?'

'Come in, Paterson, sit down and have a cigarette,' said a tall, stooping, grey-haired Scot. He pushed a box across the desk, then leaned back in his swivel chair.

'How are you enjoying life down at Montreux? Are they making you comfortable?'

George laughed. 'Before the war you had to pay a lot of money for this kind of holiday.'

For a few minutes they talked about Edinburgh which both knew well, then McTavish brought the conversation back to the present.

'I suppose you're wondering what all this is in aid of?'

'You're right. I have been puzzled.'

'Well,' went on the other, 'before I explain you must understand that anything I tell you is strictly confidential.'

'Okay,' Paterson nodded.

'First of all, this press office is just a front. My real work is for S.O.E.'

His listener snapped mentally to attention. S.O.E. was, he knew, an arm of the secret service. What in hell had they to do with him?

'My particular job,' went on McTavish, 'is to send agents into Italy on special assignments. Sometimes they go in to get information that's needed back in London, sometimes it's for sabotage and quite often it's to find out what the partisans are doing and whether we can and should help.' He paused and drew reflectively on his cigarette.

'It's a tricky business. I get hundreds of appeals for arms and explosives. Some are genuine. Some from would-be racketeers who figure weapons have a resale value while others are inspired by the Fascists through their counter-agents. As you can see, I need reliable men on the ground —men who can assess a situation and let me know which are genuine requests.'

He paused. George made no comment.

'Well,' he continued, 'a particularly sensitive situation is just beginning to develop. I'll tell you a little more about it in a few minutes. It's considered important back home.'

George sat still listening.

'I had a man all ready to go in, but unfortunately he went down with meningitis four days ago and I'm afraid that he's not going to pull through. This leaves me with no one available for the job. Of course, I could get an agent specially sent out from England, but that would take considerable time and planning, and he would need a lot of briefing on conditions across the line to put him into the picture.'

George nodded, studying the other man keenly. He looked more like a pleasant, middle-aged businessman than a secret service agent.

'We have your record,' went on McTavish, 'and from

our point of view it's a very good one. You speak Italian, and you have recently lived among them and worked with the underground. I'm not going to beat about the bush. You could handle this job and we would like you to come in with us. But understand this, there is no compulsion. If you join us you come as a volunteer. If you don't want to, we say goodbye and you forget the whole interview.'

The younger man listened to the proposal with no great enthusiasm. He felt that he had had his full share of danger and hardship. Now, just when he had met Karen, they wanted him to go back. Surely he told himself, there was someone else who could do it. The older man sat silent awaiting an answer.

'Will you tell me a little more about it?' George said finally, to give himself a chance to think.

A map was produced. It showed the border country in great detail.

'Here's Lake Maggiore,' McTavish began, pointing to the long finger of water with the frontier line running through its upper half.

'Just to the west of the lake here you see how Italy pokes up into Switzerland. It's in this bulge that you would be operating. Actually it's rather like a horseshoe, about thirty-five miles each way, with mountains all round and farmland in the valley which is all part of the Toce River watershed.

'At the open end to the south, is the town of Domodossola with a German garrison and there are small detachments stationed in villages throughout the area. In the mountains at the northern part of the horseshoe, the partisans have actually managed to forget their political differences and started to co-operate. In the last few days they've surprised a number of small patrols and have managed to clear a few miles of the border. They're gaining strength rapidly and their plan is to work south, come down out of the high country, clear the plain and as soon as they are strong enough, take Domodossola.

'It may all come to nothing I grant you, but there is a chance that it could spread. As you know, there's a lot of dissatisfaction throughout the country and if North Italy were to rise in rebellion it would cut the German army's lines of supply and almost certainly force them into surrender. You can see the possibilities. That's why we have to do all we can to help them.'

George nodded. 'You say it only began two or three days ago?'

'That's right.'

'I gather, then, you knew about it beforehand?'

'Of course. I'm in fairly close contact with some of the bands. Incidentally, there are four groups here: the Liberal Democrats otherwise known as the Green Flames, the Communists, the Socialists and the Royalists. My contact is one of their leaders, a Colonel Monetta. He's a very good man, a regular Italian officer who joined the partisans after Italy surrendered last year.

'These four groups have got together and formed a command junta to direct operations, and they got in touch with me a couple of weeks ago. At the moment they are all right for weapons, but if it starts to roll and recruits swarm in we'll have to get arms, ammunition and supplies to them by air-drop. That's one of the reasons why I need a man like you right on the spot.'

'There's another?'

'Yes, this one is political. I don't know whether you realize it, but these few square miles are the first in Italy to be free and under their own control for more than twenty years. A whole generation has grown up under Mussolini and since his fall, we call the tune in the south and the Germans in the north, with this one exception. How are they going to handle themselves? Will they co-operate to govern or will they break up into factions with the possibility of civil war? This may give us some clue as to what will happen in the country as a whole once Jerry is finished. The diplomats in London and Washington are interested and want reliable reports on the way it develops politically, so whoever goes in has to be half soldier and half political observer.'

'Quite a job.'

'Yes, and believe me, a damned important one. Now as I said, George, we think you have the qualifications to handle it, but I know you've already had a pretty rough time in there and naturally you're not too keen on going back. I'm not going to press you but I would like you to think it over. Take three or four days then let me know. If it's not for you, just phone me from Montreux and we'll forget the whole business but if you feel you can do it, come back. What's today? Thursday. What about coming back next Monday morning and then we can get down to details? Is that fair enough?'

George nodded gloomily. 'I'm not making any promises.'

McTavish laughed.

CHAPTER FIFTEEN

'You're very quiet, George. A penny for your thoughts.'

He rolled over on the grass and propped himself on his elbow. 'They're not worth a penny,' he smiled. 'The heat made me drowsy and besides, that lunch you brought. *Molto buono*.'

Karen gazed at him steadily, with concern in her blue eyes. They had spent the morning climbing towards the silent purity of the high country where the meadows, small and rock encrusted, were yet soft and colourful with the blues and reds and yellows of the wild flowers. A herd of Toggenberg goats eyed them impassively through slant eyes, and seemed to be the only other living creatures. Even these, after a few moments, lost interest and went back to their browsing. Pulling out a couple of cigarettes he lighted them and passed one to Karen. She smiled her thanks and leaned back against a rock.

She's as cool and fresh now as when we started, he thought and the admiration in his eyes was plain to read.

She looked away, disconcerted, but came back to the subject.

'Darling, something's been bothering you,' she said quietly. 'Is anything wrong?'

Thoughtfully he drew on the cigarette, savouring the bite of the smoke in his throat. How right she was and he could not tell her why. His glance wandered back down the slope, the way they had come, past the dark green of spruce woods to where the lake lay, blue and unruffled under a cloudless August sky. Shimmering through the heat haze over on the further shore were the hills of France

and somewhere beyond those hills, far away in Normandy
and Brittany, armies were clawing savagely at each other
and men were dying, dying even as he lay here.

Somehow it made him feel uneasy that he should be here
with a pretty girl by his side when other men were out
there doing the fighting. No one would blame him, but he
knew he would blame himself. Besides, he admitted, trying
to be honest in his analysis, there was something about the
prospect of battle, an excitement, a fascination, that drew
most men. In a way it was rather like hunting, only a little
fairer. The deer has so little chance. But in war the odds
are roughly even, maybe even a little against you, which
adds to the thrill.

On the other hand, why be a bloody fool and rush back
into trouble? He'd had his bellyful of danger, more than
three years of it, and there were plenty who had done sweet
damn all. Also there was Karen and he knew she was the
real reason for his reluctance, the reason why the thought
of leaving made him feel hollow and empty inside. Damn
it, he loved her, so right away the bastards had to press him
into going back.

I've a good mind to tell them to go to hell, he thought,
but he knew he wouldn't. No, they were stuck, and by
rotten bad luck he was the one man who could help them.
He'd have to go this time, he decided. Next time someone
else could do the volunteering.

She sat quietly watching and waiting for him to speak.

'Karen,' he said looking up, 'you're right, something
has been worrying me. I may have to go away.'

'Go away?' Her voice sounded small. 'Where, George?'

He braced himself to lie convincingly. 'To Locarno to
work for the British Consul down there. You know that I
speak fairly good Italian.'

'But Locarno isn't far,' she broke in, relieved. 'I thought
you meant they were sending you to your regiment, over

144

there,' and she waved vaguely in the direction of France. 'You'll be able to get back here for weekends.'

'Could you come down there if I couldn't get away?'

'Of course I could.'

Instinctively he reached out and took her hand. In another instant he would have had her in his arms pouring out his love, but a cold depressing thought checked him. He was going into something desperate. He might well be dead within a month. It didn't seem fair under these circumstances to tie her to him.

'I'm going to miss you, darling,' he compromised, 'so very much.'

Next day was Monday and he once again took the morning train for Berne.

'Come in,' said McTavish with a smile, 'I thought you would be back.'

'You don't know how touch and go it was,' retorted George sourly, 'but anyway, here I am.'

'Good. Pull up a chair and we'll get down to business.'

They spent most of the day together, with McTavish briefing him in minute detail about conditions across the border, the names and backgrounds of the partisan chiefs with whom he would be working and his own identity and cover story.

'As you were under suspicion by the Gestapo in San Vittore it wouldn't be wise to go back as George Paterson, so I've had a new I.D. card and dog-tags made up for you. When you cross the frontier you become Major George Robertson of the Royal Engineers, captured in North Africa and held at Padua prisoner-of-war camp. You escaped at the time of the Italian surrender and have been with the partisans ever since. Got that?

'Now tomorrow I want you to go down to Locarno and contact John Birback, our Vice-Consul there. He's an escaped P.O.W. himself and he's also working for S.O.E.

He'll go all over this again with you and get you fitted out. You'll need mountain clothing, and at the right time he'll see that you get safely across the border. It might be a week or even a little longer before everything is laid on. Once you're over, you'll be reporting back through Birback who's your link with me.'

George nodded. 'Would it be possible,' he asked, 'for me to take another man along? My corporal in the paratroops, a fellow called Jack Watson, is down at Montreux. He's as steady as they come, speaks Italian and knows how to handle a wireless set. I think on a job like this he would be a good man to have.'

McTavish considered this. 'If you can vouch for him,' he said finally, 'and guarantee that he can keep his mouth shut, you can approach him. Remember though, there mustn't be any pressure. If he's willing to go, take him down with you tomorrow and I'll get the documents made up for him.'

That evening he tracked Watson to the hotel where he was billeted and took him to one of the outdoor cafés for a drink. After some reminiscing George approached the subject but kept the details vague.

'So that's how it is, Jack,' he concluded, 'I'm going back, but it probably won't be any picnic and it may turn into a regular snafu. I'd like to have you along, but if you don't feel like coming I won't blame you.'

Watson's decision was immediate. 'I'm with you, sir. There doesn't seem much chance of getting back to England yet and I'd sure like another crack at those damned Jerries.'

They shook on it.

'Good,' said George. 'We start in the morning.'

John Birback, a slim, dark-haired, intelligent-looking man in his early thirties, met them at Locarno.

'Glad to meet you, George. McTavish has sent me all the

gen, and I've got rooms for you both at the Albergo Sole. It's a restaurant-cum-guest-house on the lake-front. It's quiet, and the food is first class so you should be comfortable. Come on, I've got a car waiting.'

'Sounds fine. I hear you're going to fit us out with mountain gear.'

'We'll get started on that tomorrow and there's also a lot of work to be done on codes. Hope you have a good memory.'

'When do you think we'll be going over?'

'Oh, it will be some time next week before everything is laid on.'

'Would it be all right to have a friend come down for the weekend?'

Birback chuckled. 'A Swiss miss? By all means, as long as you're discreet.'

They were driving along the lake-front. 'Here's the pub,' commented their driver, slowing to a halt. 'Nicely convenient for the night life of Locarno. This is a gay little town and I'm going to be rather sorry to leave after the war.'

They dined together very well as Birback had promised and then took brandy out on the terrace to sit and talk idly of what they had each done in those distant days when there was peace, and how they had come to be captured and to escape.

The next few days were busy ones, getting Alpine outfits, sweaters, boots, breeches and suède jackets which gave them a Tyrolean appearance. Then there were maps to be studied, codes and names and detailed instructions to be memorized, and their cover stories to be developed until they were foolproof. It was almost like being at school again, thought George, and, like school, there was the weekend ahead. He had phoned Karen and she had promised to come.

On Saturday afternoon he met her at the station, looking lovelier than ever in a simple blue dress that matched her eyes. Taking the suitcase he tucked her arm through his.

'And how's the most beautiful girl in Switzerland?' he teased, towering over her. 'Would a swim, dinner and then dancing suit my lady?'

She smiled up at him. 'Sounds wonderful.'

'Come on, then. I've got you a room in a hotel near mine.'

After dinner he took her to a lake-front cabaret where the band played soft dance music. They were happy together, yet there was an undercurrent of sad unease. It was a beautiful dream. Could it ever happen again or would the war destroy it like everything else?

At three the musicians went home, but he could not bear the thought of saying good night. Not yet.

'Let's go down to the beach,' he suggested.

They sat close together on the sand wrapped in their own thoughts, both conscious of the stillness about them, as though they were in the world alone. The moon was full and close above the encircling mountains, shining down on the water and turning its smooth surface to black and silver. The moonlight caught her, making her hair and skin a warm golden invitation that he could not resist. His arm went round her.

'My God, Karen, I've missed you.'

She came to him, unresisting, reaching up to pull his head down till their lips met and clung together.

'It's been that way for me, too,' she whispered breathlessly, tearing herself away and leaning her head on his shoulder.

But he could not stop kissing her, pressing her to him.

'Darling, you know I love you. I want to marry you, but...' He hesitated, not wanting to lie but unable to explain his mission.

'I think I know,' she said quietly, praying it wasn't so. 'You're going back into Italy, aren't you?'

He nodded.

'That's why I shouldn't have said anything to you. There's always the chance they may get me this time, but I just couldn't help myself.'

She tried to laugh, but was nearer to tears.

'Oh, darling, I love you. What are we going to do?' she cried brokenly.

He held her tight, this girl who meant everything to him and only when the night had turned to the grey of dawn did he take her back, walking hand in hand to her hotel.

On Sunday afternoon they swam again and then strolled through the park where a military band was giving a concert.

'Back in Canada this is Labour Day Weekend,' he told her, 'when you close up the summer cottage for another year and the kids are hating the thought of going back to school.'

'Do you think your people will like me?' she asked, timidly.

'Like you? They'll love you. How could they not?'

She smiled her thanks and said unhappily, 'I think we had better get my suitcase now or I'll miss that train. It's the last one today.'

Standing on the platform, straining for a last glimpse as she waved from the carriage window, he felt an empty feeling in the pit of his stomach. When would he see her again? Everything had conspired to separate them. Why the hell couldn't he have had a nice peacetime romance, when he could see his girl every day and never wonder if this would be the last time?

There was a message waiting for him at the hotel. Jack Watson had taken the call.

'It was John Birback. Says that arrangements are almost complete and it will be tomorrow or the day after.'

'The sooner we get the job done the better I'll be pleased. Come and have a drink, Jack, I need cheering up.'

On Tuesday afternoon Birback drove up in the shiny black consular sedan.

'Okay, chaps,' he greeted them, 'it's all laid on for this afternoon. Have you got your stuff ready?'

The drive should have been delightful through mountainous country past neat, prosperous-looking farmhouses in upland valleys where men and women worked peacefully in the fields, but the grey spectre of the last three years reminded the Canadian that only a few miles away there was war and hatred, hunger and death.

After an hour's driving Birback pulled into the side of the road. 'We're getting near the frontier now so I'll take down the flag. No use advertising our presence.'

A few more miles and they pulled in to a squat, red-brick frontier post where their arrival seemed to be expected. A young pleasant-faced lieutenant came out and welcomed them.

'Are these the two gentlemen who wish to go back across the border?'

Birback nodded. 'These are the two, Lieutenant.'

'You both understand, of course, that having once left Switzerland, if you should again return you will be much more closely confined?'

'That's been explained to us,' George assured him.

'Good. Well, if you're ready I'll go with you to the frontier. It's just in the middle of the bridge down there. I think some of your friends are waiting on the far side. As you know, the partisans have got control in this area.'

Saying goodbye to Birback, they walked with the officer down the road to the bridge which spanned a small ravine. Reaching it, he stopped.

'This is where I say goodbye,' he said, shaking their hands. 'Good luck to both of you.'

With a brief word of thanks they turned and strode across the bridge, back into combat.

CHAPTER SIXTEEN

THREE men were waiting on the further side. Two, roughly dressed, with rifles slung across their shoulders, appeared to be peasants, but the third, though similarly clad, had an obvious air of authority. He was a middle-aged man, lean, grey-haired, with a bristling moustache and the look of a soldier. Stepping forward, hand outstretched, he greeted George.

'Major Robertson, let me welcome you to Free Italy. I'm Colonel Monetta, formerly of the Royal Sardinian cavalry, and I am to be your liaison officer with our partisan brigades.'

George took an immediate liking to the man. He looked tough and resolute and there was something honest and steadfast in his grey-blue eyes.

'I'm delighted to be here,' he replied, not altogether truthfully, 'and very pleased to be able to work with so distinguished a soldier. This is my wireless operator and bodyguard, Corporal Watson.'

'The brigadiers are coming in to Malesco to meet you,' continued Monetta when the introductions were completed. 'It's only a couple of miles along the road. I'm sorry we haven't got transport, but only a few trucks have been captured so far and they're out with the different bands.'

Their way led round the shoulder of a mountain along a road bordered by low, rough-built stone walls beyond which there were vineyards and an occasional small white-washed cottage. There was activity in the village. Fifteen or twenty roughly dressed mountaineers each with a rifle or pistol strapped to his belt, lounged about outside the largest house. They were led inside, where the band leaders with their chief lieutenants awaiting them.

George was introduced to the principals. The first was Superbi, leader of the Socialists, a round, jolly man, fat and comfortable looking. Very different were Arca and DiDio, leaders of the Green Flames and Royalist bands. These two were young, enthusiastic ex-army officers, both with little knowledge of politics, but possessed of a burning desire to rid Italy of the Tedeschi.

'Our Communist friend, Moscatelli, has sent word that he's too busy to come,' DiDio told him after he had shaken hands all round. 'Probably too busy trying to turn the peasants into Reds, if the truth were known.'

The other two leaders nodded in angry agreement and George surmized that there was little love lost between Moscatelli and the other chieftains.

'Ah, well,' said Superbi after a slight pause, 'as he's not here he's not here. Sit down, Major, and have a drink.' With that he lowered himself on to a bench and picked up a half-empty mug of vino.

George was given a glass of wine and a chair and after an enthusiastic toast to 'Victory', gave a short talk, congratulating them on their past success and promising the future co-operation of the Allied governments. This was well received with smiles and nods of approval, and Arca came over to slap his shoulder.

'It is good that you have come today, Major. Tomorrow at dawn Superbi and I are going to attack an outpost where there's a garrison of these German pigs. You'll see that we mean business.'

'Splendid. I'd like to come along and see the fun.'

It was arranged that he would spend the night at Arca's headquarters a few miles to the east, and when the meeting broke up he went off with the Green Flames along with Watson, Monetta and a couple of well-armed characters who had been added to his entourage as bodyguards and runners.

Before dawn they were in position on the high ground above the outpost, a small, undistinguished village which spread across the entrance to a narrow valley.

'Superbi's men are on the other side,' explained Arca as they lay together behind one of the low stone walls that criss-crossed the countryside.

It was a grey misty morning, but they could make out the buildings below.

'You see that big house over to the right with the barn underneath? That's where the Tedeschi are quartered. We'll start stirring them up now.'

He nodded to one of his guards who was crouched near by and the man, hurriedly aiming, let off a shot. Almost immediately it was answered by a fusillade from Superbi's men on the other hill. A face peered out from one of the upstairs windows, then disappeared again as rifles cracked up and down the hillside. For a few minutes there was silence from the German position, but then, as though getting over their first surprise, they began to return the fire and George instinctively ducked as a bullet whistled close overhead.

'Here, give me that rifle,' he ordered one of his bodyguards who was firing rounds with more enthusiasm than care.

Taking the weapon and sighting carefully he let off several rounds at one of the windows. It was impossible to tell whether he had hit anything, but he felt better and returned the weapon to its impatient owner.

The battle continued for ten or fifteen minutes without casualties to the Italians, until one man was hit in the shoulder. Then on the terrace below another partisan jerked and flopped over backwards, a slow trickle of blood oozing from a mortal wound in the middle of his forehead.

Suddenly something appeared at one of the farmhouse windows. It was a kitchen broom with a man's white shirt attached.

'Look, look,' called several voices, 'they've surrendered.'

'Stop shooting. Stop shooting,' bellowed Arca. 'Pass the word along.'

After a minute or so both hillsides relapsed into silence and then the farm door opened and a line of German soldiers, hands over their heads, filed out. Like boys suddenly released from school, the partisans rushed down the hillsides, whooping, hallooing, racing with each other to be first to reach the prisoners.

The Germans were a sorry and frightened lot, about twenty of them, commanded by a middle-aged sergeant. They had with them a couple of wounded and one dead man.

'Kamerad. Kamerad,' they kept repeating, fearful that their throats were going to be slit.

'What are you going to do with them?' Paterson asked Superbi who had just panted up.

'Oh, we'll take their equipment and put them across the border into Switzerland.'

After an hour's heated discussion as to the fair distribution of weapons, ammunition and food, the bands dispersed to their own areas. The captives were marched off under strong guard, while George and his group returned to Malesco where he planned to make his temporary quarters.

During the next couple of weeks the partisans worked south, coming down from the mountains into the valley of the Toce River and mopping up the isolated German detachments as they progressed. These detachments, never more than a platoon in strength, put up little resistance and seemed to be overawed by the size of the forces against them.

'Just as well,' thought Paterson grimly, for his new friends, kind and hospitable as they were, had with few exceptions not the slightest idea of war and could have been badly mauled by a determined foe. He was rather surprised that the enemy had not reacted more strongly and almost every day expected to hear that a German fighting battalion had moved into the area. But as this did not happen he guessed that every front-line soldier was tied down, trying to stem the Allied advance from the South.

The partisans were slowly moving forward, averaging three or four miles in a good day. When they didn't move, George visited the four brigades and their commanders, including Moscatelli. He was impressed by his driving force. Of the other leaders, Arca and DiDio were strictly military men, while Superbi was a politician who readily admitted that he was no soldier. In fact, if he hadn't had a good second-in-command, Superbi would have been in serious trouble. On the other hand, Moscatelli, a stocky, powerfully built man of about thirty-five, was both soldier and politician. He was a product of the Milan slums, for a long time an opponent of the régime, who had only recently returned from Moscow, travelling through Yugoslavia.

He had been highly trained during his stay with the Russians in both guerrilla tactics and political activity, and aided by a powerfully built lieutenant who had an evil reputation for solving political differences with a bullet, he had enjoyed great success in mobilizing or conscripting the peasants of his area into the Communist brigade. It was by far the largest unit, about two thousand men, while the others had about five hundred each. George noted that, despite Moscatelli's drive and determination, his force, like the others, lacked trained officers and N.C.O.s, and was equally disorganized and unpredictable.

The Communist leader returned the other brigadiers' distrust and dislike in good measure, though this was not particularly unusual, for as far as Paterson could determine they were all mutually mistrustful. In addition, Moscatelli despised his fellows, being supremely confident that he was the only one who knew where he was going and how he would get there.

'Mark my words,' he answered George, 'after the war the workers will run this country and you'll see Italy with a Communist government. We're the party of the future.'

By the latter half of September they were closing in on Domodossola, the only fair-sized town in the area, situated at the open base of the horseshoe in gently rolling country. There were about two hundred German soldiers in the town, quite sufficient if they wished to put up a stiff and possibly successful defence, but the partisan leaders, fresh from their minor victories, were supremely confident as their columns closed round the town and cut the road to Novara and the South.

Once the trap was closed bullets began to pour in upon the beleaguered centre from all sides and this was answered by the chatter of spandaus and the crackle of small-arms fire. The battle continued for a while, and then the German commander, feeling that his honour was satisfied, hoisted a white bedsheet above the town hall in token of surrender. This lack of fighting spirit puzzled George until he had a chance to see the prisoners, a sorry lot, mostly elderly reservists, unwilling conscripts who by no stretch of the imagination could be considered front-line troops. In addition, there were fifty or sixty Ukranians who had been drafted into the Wehrmacht and who were now quite ready to throw in their lot with the partisans, just so long as someone fed them. Their offer was accepted and they did quite well, being the only disciplined troops in the whole rebel army.

With the taking of Domodossola the bands seemed content to sit back and rest upon their laurels. They were, almost without exception, parochially minded. This was their land. They had freed it and now the job was to guard it. As for the rest of the country, that was someone else's responsibility. To Paterson such a policy spelt disaster. These three thousand lightly armed and undisciplined men couldn't stand up against any sort of organized attack. Their only hope was to keep advancing, employ hit-and-run tactics and spread the uprising until it became too big to be stamped out, instead of sitting here and waiting to be picked off when the Germans were good and ready. He emphasized this point at the councils of war, but he could not push his views too far, for he was merely an observer and an adviser.

The commanders gave lip service to his idea of attack. Possibly they believed in it themselves, but they could only go as far and as fast as their men would allow. Each was suspicious that if they should advance one of the others might gain control here.

George had an example of this hostility one evening when he drove up with Arca to visit the Green Flames' headquarters. Their road lay through some of Moscatelli's territory, and as they drove along in the half-light a shot was fired at them from a scrub-covered hillside. It hit the truck just behind Arca, fortunately missing him.

The bodyguard tumbled out and went in pursuit, but the would-be assassin had disappeared.

'Comrade Moscatelli is trying to solve his problems,' commented Arca dryly.

'I think,' said Superbi at the end of one long and heated council meeting, 'that we should first organize the government of this liberated territory and put the whole area in a state of defence. Then, with this as our base we can advance.'

George felt cynical. Superbi, the bon-vivant, had requisitioned a comfortable house with a good wine supply and he had installed a pretty mistress. Who would want to advance from that?

News of their drive down the Toce Valley had been sent through Switzerland to the Allied-controlled Italian government in the South, and they had immediately sent a representative to act in their interest as administrator in the area. He arrived early one morning, brought in by men from one of the outposts after having travelled up from Rome through the length of German-held territory. A mild little man with gold-rimmed spectacles and a university background that earned him the appellation of Professor, he immediately set about organizing an administration with a governing council drawn half from the partisan bands and half from the civilian population of the town and surrounding countryside.

Troubles were to beset this body, but at its first meeting good news was received. A company of Arca's men guarding a section of the Lake Maggiore shoreline, their eastern boundary, spotted a small armada crossing from the opposite shore. It proved to be several launches towing a number of barges crowded with Fascist infantry. The Green Flames organized an ambush and, as the boats came in to beach, they opened a withering fire, killing and wounding many of the Fascists who retreated across the lake in great disorder.

Despite this good news there were grave problems for the embryo government in Domodossola. Captured ammunition was running short and the military half of the junta was so concerned about this that it seemed even less likely they would strike out until they had fresh supplies. Then there was the question of food. No one had any money to feed more than three thousand very hungry partisans. Cattle and supplies were commandeered much to the annoyance of the peasant farmers and civilian members of the council while the Professor, caught in the middle, had increasing difficulty in keeping the various factions from each other's throats.

'I think the best thing I can do is take a trip back to Locarno,' decided George at one such angry meeting. 'It will be quicker that way to arrange air-drops of weapons and ammo, and I can tell them that we desperately need money to pay for supplies.'

The Professor nodded. 'Very good, Giorgio. Impress on them that a government without money is like a well without water.'

A truck was quickly found to take him thirty miles up to Malesco. Colonel Monetta, who was accompanying him this far, arranged with one of the villagers to guide him across the frontier to the nearest railway station, several miles beyond the border.

'The Signore can catch the milk train which goes at four in the morning,' suggested a grizzled but shrewd mountaineer. 'We won't leave here until one, so you can get some sleep. I'll wake you.'

They crossed the frontier about half a mile east of the bridge over which he had come into Italy, and then walked another mile along a hillside slope before striking a road. The journey was uneventful, with no sign of the Swiss border patrol. Soon after three he was at the station.

'I'll get your ticket,' offered the old man, 'the stationmaster is a good friend of mine.'

At Locarno, a taxi whisked him through the light early morning traffic out to the Albergo Sole where mine host greeted him like a long-lost brother. Because of the war, visitors were rare and business deplorable.

'Tell me what I can do for you, Signore. The Albergo Sole is at your service.'

'Right at the moment I need a room and a hot bath, and then if you've got anything good for breakfast, I'm starved.'

After a shave, a bath and a meal, he felt fine. There was a phone in the bar. He must get in touch with Birback, but he'd have a drink first.

As he sat on the high stool relaxed and full of well-being, the swing door to the street opened and a young couple entered, an officer in uniform and a very pretty girl. Idly he glanced at them and then with a sudden start, turned hurriedly away. It was the lieutenant who had escorted him to the border a month ago. If he was recognized he could be arrested for re-entering the country and that would certainly louse up the plan.

Hunched over his drink, back carefully turned to the new arrivals, he awaited developments.

The barman took the couple's order, then came over to him.

'I beg your pardon, Signore, but the Lieutenant would like to speak to you.'

Oh damn, he thought, I'm for it now.

The Swiss looked up smiling as he came across. 'Back from your travels,' he greeted, with the slightest of winks. 'My fiancée and I would be delighted if you would have a drink with us.'

After a friendly chat, in which any reference to border crossing was carefully avoided, he excused himself and phoned Birback.

'This is a pleasant surprise, George. I'll be right over.'

'You've done splendidly,' commended Birback when they finished. 'I'll get all this information typed and sent to headquarters. As to the money and ammunition, that won't be any problem. We'll get off a code telegram to London laying down the air-drops and I'll phone McTavish to send money. It should all be arranged by tomorrow. Now, what are you doing tonight? Well, some friends of mine are throwing a party. What about coming along? I'll pick you up about nine.'

Before he went out that evening, he phoned Karen. It took some time to get the call through to Montreux, but finally he heard her voice at the other end of the line.

'Hello, my love. How are you?'

'George, oh, how wonderful. Where are you?'

'I'm in Locarno and missing you like the very devil.'

She laughed. 'That makes two of us, but now you're back, everything is going to be all right. When will I see you?'

'I can't make it this time, honey. I've got to go back tomorrow, it's just a rush trip.'

'Go back?' All the sparkle went out of her voice. 'But, darling, you've done your share. Why can't someone else go this time? I just couldn't stand it if anything happened to you.' She broke down and began to sob.

'Sweetheart, sweetheart,' he tried to soothe her, over a hundred miles of wire, 'nothing is going to happen to me. I'm taking lots of care and pretty soon I'll be back for good. Then we'll get married.'

Gradually she stopped crying, but her voice was flat and depressed, without the gaiety that he loved.

'Goodbye, darling,' she said finally after they had said all that could be said over a phone. 'I'm sorry I was so silly, but I'm frightened for you. Please come back soon.'

He heard the receiver click. Moodily he sat smoking, thinking of her and her words. It was a mistake to phone, he decided. Now we are both upset.

All next day he hung about with little to do. He was catching a late train back. Birback was going to meet him at the hotel at eleven with the money and a man to guide him across the frontier. Until then he was on his own.

After dinner he wandered down to the cabaret where he had taken Karen only a month ago and sat at the bar, drinking cognac and thinking of the evening they had spent together. Then they had been in a little world of their own while the other couples had been no more than vague, unheeded shadows. Now he was the unheeded shadow, the outsider.

Lonely and depressed he walked along the beach to where they had lingered and told each other of their love. Somehow he expected comfort from this, but everything was different. The lake that had been so smooth was now rough and angry, while a cold east wind came out of the black and starless night to chill and buffet him.

Is this an ill omen for our future? he wondered with a shiver. 'Oh, hell,' he swore, trying to banish fancy. It's getting late and I've had too much to drink. Better return to the hotel and get ready.

CHAPTER SEVENTEEN

Birback was waiting with another man in his room. 'Got here a little early,' he explained, 'so we came on up. This is Carlo who knows the frontier. He'll get you across safely.'

The guide, a taciturn individual, moved over to the window while the other two sat on the bed.

'Here's the schedule of air-drops,' said Birback, passing him a typed sheet of onion skin. 'I don't need to remind you to be careful with it. And here,' he continued, picking up a rucksack from the bed, 'is the money, twenty million lire. That should keep you going for a while.'

George whistled. 'Twenty million lire. That's a lot. Nearly 200,000 dollars. I'll be glad to get it safely to Domodossola.'

Birback laughed. 'I know how you feel. I've been sitting on it all afternoon.' He looked at his watch. 'I'll run you to the station. Be sure to keep me posted on everything that is happening down there. Any messages you want to send for Karen I'll pass along and see that you get her replies when I have a courier going your way.'

The return journey was without incident until they reached the border. Carlo had obviously made this trip many times before and he led the way confidently as they approached the ravine which formed the boundary between the two countries. Then suddenly a man stepped out from the black mass of a clump of trees.

'Halt!' came the peremptory command and they heard a rifle bolt click. They froze as a figure approached, weapon at the ready. As he neared them George could make out the Swiss army uniform.

Twenty million lire is going to take some explaining was the thought that flashed through his mind.

'This man's an Italian refugee,' lied Carlo. 'His wife is dying in Malesco and I'm taking him back to be near her.'

The frontier guard seemed undecided. It was obvious from his questions that he was on the watch for cigarette smugglers, but as Carlo was carrying nothing and George had only the small rucksack he finally accepted their story and waved them on.

'I hope you find your wife better,' he said sympathetically, as they left him.

Reaching Malesco before dawn, George shook the protesting Monetta into action.

'I'm toting a fortune on my back, Colonel,' he explained, 'and the sooner we get it down to Domodossola, the better. Can you find us a truck?'

'Ah, Giorgio,' sighed the Colonel, lacing up his heavy boots, 'this is a hell of an hour to wake a man.'

While he was gone, searching for a vehicle, the woman of the house, who had been roused by their conversation, brought him some rolls and a cup of excellent coffee, undoubtedly contraband, for his breakfast.

In Domodossola where he officially handed over the currency, the Canadian found himself the hero of the hour. The Professor was ecstatic to the point of embracing him.

'Now that we have money we can truly organize a government.'

Even Moscatelli, normally aloof and suspicious, conceded that this was a token of good faith on the part of Russia's allies and grudgingly congratulated George. As far as the air-drops were concerned, all four brigadiers were delighted at the prospect of strengthening their fire-power.

The Green Flames were to receive the first consignment three days hence, and on that night George, Arca and a dozen of his men with two trucks camped on the drop area, a flat-topped hill to the north of Domodossola. It was cold as they squatted round a fire; the night was clear and their plane should have no difficulty spotting its target. About midnight they saw the long bright fingers of searchlights and heard the faint sound of guns from far to the south.

'Must be a raid on down there. Somebody's getting hell.'

When their drop was due the hour came and went with no throb of plane engines. One-thirty, then two and George began to pace up and down in his impatience.

Damn the Air Force he thought. Not only was he missing a good night's sleep but yesterday, for the first time since they had captured Domodossola some German activity had been reported to the south and he wanted to get this fresh equipment and ammunition into partisan hands as quickly as possible.

By four o'clock they knew there was no hope for that night.

'I'm sorry,' he told Arca, 'but something went wrong somewhere.'

'Don't worry, Giorgio,' laughed the leader. 'If things ever went right in this war, then we would really be concerned. Let's go back to town and have breakfast. We will try again three nights from now.'

After sleeping until well into the afternoon, George awoke to ominous news. The partisans were dug in some ten to fifteen miles south of the town, along a good defensive line and reports had been coming in all morning of probing attacks on their positions. There had been nothing serious yet. One or two tanks, several platoons of infantry and some dive-bombing, with all the men, especially the Ukranians, putting up a good fight. But George realized, even if many of the others didn't, that this was only a preliminary to something bigger.

Moscatelli was one of the few who understood the situation. 'I've pulled back all my forward patrols,' he told

George, 'and we'll see if we can hold them. If not, we'll go back and fight in the mountains.'

The Canadian nodded. 'I'm going to take a run down first thing in the morning and see what's happening. I'll let you know what the situation looks like.'

He was never to take the trip. In the small hours of the night, Monetta roused him with bad news.

'Wake up, wake up,' he urged as the younger man struggled into a sitting position. 'Word has just come down from Malesco that a whole German battalion, Alpine troops, and some Fascist infantry have got across Lake Maggiore and landed near Canobbio. We had a patrol in the area and they could do nothing but fall back into the mountains. They blew the bridge through the pass and that may slow the Germans down a little. DiDio is up there, assembling his brigade at Malesco, and he's going to move forward at dawn to try and halt them in the pass. If we don't stop them there, they'll be in behind us along the frontier and then...' He drew a finger across his throat expressively.

Shocked into complete wakefulness by the gravity of the news, George pondered the situation briefly. The thrusts from the south were probably feints and if the Royalists couldn't stop them at the point where the bridge was blown, they could never hope to hold a force that size in the open country beyond. Could DiDio assemble his boys before the Germans arrived?

'I think we'd better get up there and see what's going on,' he told Monetta. 'I'll rouse Jack Watson while you get a car.'

They reached Malesco soon after daylight, but the partisan brigade had already marched out on the road to Canobbio.

'I'll drop you here, Jack, no point in your coming forward. If the Jerrys should knock us to hell and gone, you nip back across the frontier and let John Birback know what's happened.'

'Good luck, sir,' said Watson, shaking hands.

They drove on a few miles overtaking and passing the long straggling column of five or six hundred men, mostly Royalists but reinforced by some detachments from the Green Flames.

'The brigadier went on ahead with some of the officers,' he was told. 'Only left a few minutes ago so you should be able to catch him.'

Slipping the Fiat into gear, George drove on. They hadn't gone much over a mile when coming round the bend of a hill, they spotted the Royalist chieftain's car, parked at the side of the road with DiDio himself carefully studying the ground ahead from the vantage point of an outcrop of rock.

They were at the edge of an open valley, a rather desolate stretch of country a mile across, bordered on the further side by a line of low mountains, beyond which lay the shore of Lake Maggiore.

'Follow the line of the road,' instructed DiDio after he had greeted the newcomers. 'Do you see over on the far side how it disappears into that cleft between the hills? That's the pass. A few hundred yards along is the bridge that we blew. It all looks quiet, so I think we've beaten the Tedeschi.'

Both Paterson and Monetta studied the ground professionally. The brooding mountains were menacing in their silence, but there was no sign of troops, no sign of movement. The thin grey ribbon of road was bare of all traffic. The Colonel nodded as though satisfied with what he saw.

'The good God is with us today,' he agreed.

'We're going on to reconnoitre the bridge,' continued DiDio. 'If it's not too badly blown we might get the brigade across and set up our positions further ahead. Do you want to come with us, Giorgio?'

George thought it was folly for the commander and his senior officers to push on so far ahead, doing a job that could be better handled by a scouting patrol, but he could see that DiDio and the others were set on going. Any hesitation on his part might be misinterpreted.

'Okay,' he agreed, '*in bocca al lupo*.'*

They piled into two cars, ten of them, and sped across the deserted valley. At the entrance to the defile that was almost a canyon, the leading vehicle pulled to a halt.

'This is the last place we can turn,' explained DiDio getting out. 'We'll leave the cars here and walk. It's only five or six hundred yards along.'

The road from here on had been blasted out. A cliff rose on the left, while on the outer side, where the ground dropped away sharply, there was a low, stone guard wall. In less than ten minutes they were up to the bridge, a small, fairly modern concrete structure much more badly damaged than the reports had indicated.

'Your boys did a damn good demolition job,' commended Paterson surveying the mass of wreckage. 'I wouldn't advise trying to take your brigade across. What remains could come down at any minute.'

The Brigadier agreed. 'We'll dig in on the ridge above and catch the bastards as they come along.'

Both men strolled over and sat on the wall, lighting cigarettes. Glancing far back along the road, they could see the snakelike column of the brigade debouching on to open ground. 'We'll just finish these, then we'll head back to meet them.'

Old Monetta, unshaven and looking more grizzled than ever, joined them.

* 'Into the mouth of the wolf.'

'Strange we haven't seen or heard anything of their forward patrols. The Tedeschi usually...'

He got no further when all hell broke loose. From somewhere high on the ridge heavy machine-guns stuttered into life. It was so unexpected that for seconds they just sat, confused by the mounting crescendo of noise as echoes began to multiply and remultiply the sound. Then they saw the distant column disintegrate into a multitude of running figures as the fire tore into the ranks and the men dived for safety.

'Look out,' shouted one of the partisans as bullets splattered against the cliff wall on the other side of the road, 'they're on the other hill too. Get down behind the wall.'

They began to crawl back towards the cars, while the machine-guns intermittently peppered the wall and the cliff.

'For God's sake, Giorgio,' yelled DiDio who was immediately behind him, 'keep your backside down.'

He cursed but flattened himself, struggling with the tommy-gun which kept flopping off his shoulder. The firing and the echoes were increasing in intensity as the battle opened up. There was the slow beat of heavy machine-guns, the rat-tat-tat of light ones mixed with the sound of Italian Bredas. That would be the Blackshirt company which was with the Germans.

After a while he heard heavier reports, twelve-point-sevens and twenty-millimetres, he guessed. They must have kept a lot of their stuff down behind the ridge out of sight. Now they were bringing them forward.

Across the valley the partisans, obviously stunned by the suddenness of the attack, were beginning to answer back. A few machine-guns burst into life and there was some scattered rifle fire.

Good lads, he thought, they're doing their best.

On they went, half dragging themselves, half crawling. At the moment the enemy above were out of sight and all they had to worry about were those on the other hill, but once they reached the entrance to the canyon they would be out on open ground where they would be exposed to a hail of fire. He thought of this as he crawled along, but only in passing. His chief concern at the moment was to keep down behind the wall, and to keep moving.

It took them more than half an hour to work their way back to the cars. Meantime the enemy had pushed forward along the hilltop so that now the two Fiats were in their line of fire. As he watched, tracers began striking them, first one and then the other. Glass shattered, there were wisps of smoke and then flames as the petrol tanks were hit.

Cautiously he surveyed the ground immediately ahead. There was an open area twenty yards across where the cars stood and which was now stitched by bursts of machine-gun fire. This had to be crossed. Immediately beyond was dead ground that was still safe. On its far side another open stretch ended where a big cement storm culvert ran under the road. After that there was no more cover and any further movement would be suicide. The culvert would at least offer some shelter. There was always the faint hope of some unexpected development that might give them a chance to escape.

Several partisans at the head of the crawling line had got across the bad stretches before the guns had been able to bear, and now they were huddled in the culvert. As he watched, two more made a dash during a lull in the firing, and they made it.

A third man, encouraged by this followed. He reached the dead ground. But as he did so the hail of bullets began again. He was safe where he was. For some reason he tried to cover the last section. He hadn't taken more than two paces before he crumpled to the ground and lay motionless.

At the next lull Monetta sprinted across the first open space and dived for cover, just ahead of the bullets snapping at his heels.

It was now George's turn, then DiDio and his runner. He waited as minutes passed, five, ten. Several times, the fire slackening, he made ready to go. Then it would begin again and he eased back to the ground.

My God, they've got a hate on, he thought grimly.

Finally it slowed, then ceased. This was the moment, and with it came a sudden fear. In a few seconds he could be dead. He thought of the twenty-millimetre firing from the opposite hill. If they turned it on the wall it would knock one hell of a big hole in it and him. He had to go.

Grasping his tommy-gun he sprang forward, expecting to feel the sudden hammerlike blow of a bullet that would smash him to the ground. In a furious burst of energy he covered the twenty yards, then dived for cover beside Monetta who had waited for him. As he hit the earth, DiDio was rising to follow him. He came to his feet and took his first leap as the machine-guns began to chatter again. He stumbled, an awful look of agony crossed his white face and his hand went to his left knee as he went down. He lay there in the middle of the road with a smashed knee. His comrades watched in helpless horror as the Germans cut him to pieces, making his dead body jerk convulsively.

'Jesus,' muttered George, stunned by the suddenness of the tragedy. DiDio, only twenty-four, had been his good friend, a loyal and courageous comrade, who had ably commanded hundreds of men. He was the finest type of Italian.

Monetta, looking grey and old, tugged at his sleeve. 'Come on, Giorgio, we can do no good here.'

He nodded. DiDio's runner, the last man, had shouted out that he was staying where he was rather than risk crossing the open space, so the sooner they joined the others the better.

Another momentary lull when the guns lifted to take on more distant targets gave them their awaited chance to join the five others who had reached the temporary safety of the culvert.

George cautiously examined the terrain from both ends. The upper side faced the slope on which the Germans were positioned, but was shielded to a certain extent by some boulders and outcrops of rock. The lower end was also sheltered by a number of large rocks, but beyond there was a barren field which sloped away for several hundred yards without any sign of cover.

He grinned wryly at old Monetta. 'I wonder what the military textbooks say about this sort of situation.'

The older man scowled and slapped the butt of his submachine-gun. 'All we can do is try to take some of the bastards with us.'

They sat back to await developments while the firing continued from both sides. If the partisans could hold their position and keep the Germans pinned down on this side of the valley until nightfall, they might just have a chance of getting back under cover of darkness, but George knew it was the slimmest of chances. There were hours of daylight left and it seemed to him that partisan fire was slowly but perceptibly slackening while from above they heard the reports of new and heavier guns. Now eighty-eights were shelling their positions and a forty-seven-millimetre anti-tank gun was trying to get at them. It couldn't actually bear on the culvert, but it was shattering rocks above them and bombarding the entrance with flying pieces of rock.

They huddled at the lower end, trying to avoid rock

splinters and the occasional ricochet that whined into the tunnel. Little hope was left in any of them. Money, documents and letters were destroyed. They rechecked tommy-guns, hand grenades and the remaining ammunition.

The battle went on for about two hours, then firing began to slow down until finally it ceased altogether. There was a strange, unnatural silence. They had some rations with them and now they nibbled, not because they were hungry but rather to reduce the mounting tension. Only Monetta broke the silence with an irritated snarl at the youngest partisan, a boy of no more than eighteen.

'For God's sake, lad, get ready to fight like the devil.'

Suddenly they heard something close by. A rock fell and started a stream of pebbles. Almost at the same instant footsteps sounded on the road above.

Monetta and another man moved slowly to the mouth of the culvert where they crouched listening. Then everything happened at once. Both men jumped out and let go with long sweeping bursts while the others erupted after them. No orders were given. No orders were needed.

Their position was hopeless. This type of fighting was known for its savage and bitter quality. No quarter was expected, while to be wounded was only a slower sentence of death. As George came out of the culvert two grenades went off almost in his face. Fortunately they were Italian red jobs which did little more than create a flash, a lot of noise and give a man a bad scare. A piece from one nicked the inside of his wrist, but in the mad fury of the moment he ignored it.

Flinging himself behind a boulder he noticed that two of their group were making a dash for it down the hill. Thirty yards from the road they paused an instant and let go with their sub-machine-guns. Then they raced on again, but one had only taken a few paces when he was caught in a burst from an unseen German higher on the hillside. He jerked, turned about and collapsed while his comrade raced on disappearing from sight in a patch of dead ground.

A German in the green uniform of the Alpine troops forgot caution as he fired after the running partisan. George raised his gun quickly, but before he had time to fire there was a staccato stutter on his left and the German shuddered, dropped his rifle and slumped, slowly sliding forward over a boulder.

'That's one to go with me,' yelled old Monetta with a cold grin, as he wriggled into a new position.

There was no time for congratulations. More grenades exploded. Then George spotted one of the enemy creeping from boulder to boulder occasionally outlined against the sky. He got off a short burst which caught the man in the chest. And that one's for me, he thought.

There was less movement now. Everyone was out of sight except Monetta, who had stayed close beside him. Suddenly there came a burst from close at hand. He whipped round to see Monetta sagging down with his head in a shallow pool of water while blood was beginning to stain his jacket from three or four holes in his side.

Lying quiet for a moment, trying to estimate from where the shots had come, George began to squirm and crawl round the angle of a rock. There he was, the man who had killed old Monetta, peering cautiously over a boulder not fifteen yards away, his head in profile. Quietly lifting his tommy-gun and carefully aiming, George let go a vicious burst, and before the man crumpled he saw with satisfaction the gaping wound that suddenly appeared in his head. Another for company, Monetta.

Letting go at fleeting targets with several more bursts he was trying to crawl further away from the road when he caught sight of another German, this time in full view over on the right. Raising his weapon he quickly squeezed the trigger. Nothing happened.

'Damn—blast—no ammunition.'

This was it. The others were all dead and within a few minutes, if he remained crouched here defenceless, he would join them. There was just one very slim chance. Throwing aside his useless gun he stood up, getting ready to feel the burst that would be the end.

He had only a few seconds before the Germans were on him, angered by their losses and out for blood. Grabbing his arms, they began kicking and punching vindictively while one caught him across the side of the head with a rifle butt. He felt the warm blood trickle down his cheek. Dazed and staggering, he was roughly flung back against a large rock with such force that he lost consciousness.

CHAPTER EIGHTEEN

WHAT now, he wondered dully as he came to with a splitting head, fighting back waves of nausea. Two of the enemy stepped back several feet and he heard them cock their rifles.

'Hold it, hold it, you stupid dolts.'

It was a roar that made both George and his captors jump. He glanced up and saw a man striding briskly down the hillside, a big imposing figure in the uniform of a sergeant-major of Alpine troops.

The Germans snapped to attention as the warrant-officer stormed up.

'Who told you to shoot prisoners?' he demanded. 'Don't you fools realize that they can give us information? Take him back to camp and see that he doesn't escape.'

The men grouped about him and with a rifle in his back, prodded him towards the road. As they went by Monetta's body one of the men, pulling out a Luger, savagely put three shots into the dead Italian's head, then quickly went through his pockets. But finding nothing of value he cursed obscenely, took off the dead man's boots and hurried on.

Back on the road George looked about. He counted ten dead Germans sprawled on the scene of the battle and all the partisans who had been with him in the culvert except for the man who had fled down the hill. Maybe he had escaped.

We made them pay, he thought grimly; no wonder they wanted to shoot me.

Another group of the enemy joined them with a prisoner, DiDio's courier, who had stayed at the mouth of

the defile and been picked up there. Together they were
hustled up the hill slope, over the ridge, and down into the
small valley beyond where the Germans had a bivouac and
George, as he was urged along, used the time to go over his
cover story.

I'm Major George Robertson, escaped from P.O.W.
camp Padua a year ago last September, and I've been hiding in North Italy ever since.

There were only a few troops in the bivouac. Most of the
regiment had advanced across the valley in pursuit of the
fleeing partisans, and these hastened over to stare and fling
abuse at the captives. This George tried to ignore until
suddenly one of the men stepped out from the others and
pushed up to him, staring intently.

'Ober-lieutenant Paterson,' he shouted in sudden recognition, and then broke into excited German which George
could not follow. But there was no need. He had recognized the other.

It was Willi, one of the soldiers who had been doing a
tour of guard duty at San Vittore while he was there. He
remembered the man distinctly, a loutish fellow not as
brutal as most. But to run into him again at this moment
would shoot his cover story all to hell. He'd have to revert
to being George Paterson again, and just hope they
wouldn't send him back to San Vittore.

An S.S. sergeant questioned him, but the interrogation
was brief. He only had to confirm Willi's testimony that he
was indeed Lieutenant Paterson, and had escaped from
prison some three and a half months ago. There was no
point in denying this now and as long as he could keep
them from knowing that he had crossed into Switzerland,
they just might treat him as an escaped prisoner rather
than a spy. Fortunately he wasn't searched or the forged
identity card would have made an embarrassing complication. He must destroy it at the first opportunity.

After the interview he and the courier were ordered into an open truck and guarded by half a dozen Wehrmacht, set off on the road to Canobbio on the lakeshore. It was a short drive down narrow, twisting, precipice-flaunting roads. At one point they ran into another lorry packed with Germans coming up.

It was impossible to pass and their vehicle had to back up and then pull off the road. While they were doing this the soldiers on the other truck got down. They had rifles, several carried spades. For a few sickening moments George wondered if this was an arranged rendezvous and if these men were the firing squad, who had come to this lonely place for a summary execution. However, no sharp order came to fall in. Instead they urinated, lit cigarettes, stood about talking and laughing until he realized they were just reinforcements to the front and the spades were only normal entrenching equipment.

It was evening when they reached Canobbio, an insignificant place hemmed in between the grey sullen lake and black frowning mountains. There were a lot of troops about, including black-shirted Fascists. They had little time to look before the lorry halted and they were unceremoniously prodded into a large and heavily guarded shed.

There were other prisoners there. No one he knew but several recognized him, for they came up and spoke, calling him Maggiore Giorgio which had been his name with the partisans.

They had been taken near by, so he told them of the battle and of the deaths of DiDio, Monetta and the others. There was the heavy silence that such news brings. Finally, one young fellow shrugged and gave a hard laugh.

'Well, at least they're out of it. We're in the mouth of the wolf.'

The floor was of heavy boards with cracks between.

After a time George sat down, leaned against a wall and fished out the compromising identity card, tore it into small pieces and carefully poked them, together with his dog-tags, down between the boards. As the last piece disappeared he felt safer.

Overall he was physically exhausted, worn out by the hours of battle, strain and tension. Rolling over on the bare boards he slept, never hearing the door open to admit new prisoners, nor the clatter made by the guards when they finally brought in a meagre ration of bread and black coffee. It was the raw damp cold of early dawn that finally woke him, shivering, aching, hungry and dirty.

The others were waking as well, shivering and spitting. Forcing down his feeling of disgust at this habit he turned away towards the wall.

About an hour later the door opened and they were each given a piece of bread and a mug of weak, lukewarm, black coffee. At mid-morning they were herded out, a very sorry-looking group, and loaded aboard two trucks, each guarded by half a dozen soldiers armed with sub-machine-guns. George considered the possibility of trying to escape once they were in motion, but their escort was a tough, alert-looking lot and they would have him riddled with bullets before he could hit the road.

Their way led south along the lakeshore, through villages that had once prospered on tourists but now looked bleak and almost deserted. After an hour they left Lake Maggiore and headed south for another twenty-five miles until they came to a fairly large town.

'Novara,' muttered the man beside him. 'It's my home.'

An Italian motor-cycle policeman met them on the outskirts and led them through the streets to a dirty-looking, sprawling, grey stone building that somehow had a familiar stamp.

'The prison,' confirmed the man beside him.

They were ordered into a bleak, whitewashed reception office where a clerk carefully noted their names. Then the prison warders took over and they were marched across a courtyard along several bare cement corridors to a large community cell into which they were pushed. The room was already well filled with forty or fifty men and their arrival did nothing to ease the overcrowding. But they were cheerfully greeted and eagerly questioned for news.

George looked about curiously. They were partisans from their dress and talk, but there were none that he knew personally, although he recalled having seen several of them while visiting the different bands. A man of about thirty, tough looking and powerfully built for an Italian, came over.

'I'm sorry they got you, Maggiore Giorgio,' he greeted. 'They picked me up in the fighting south of Domodossola. Got tanks in behind us and cut us off from the rest of the brigade. My name's Pico,' he went on, 'and I've seen you with General Arca.'

Pico had been a sergeant-major with an Italian paratroop unit, had fought in the desert against the Eighth Army and after Italy's collapse, had deserted and joined the partisans. He was quick-witted as well as tough and had already discovered what little information there was to be had.

'We're to be interrogated here,' he explained, 'but after that I don't know. This is only a transit prison. There's a rumour we are all going to Germany for forced labour, another that we're going to be shot. You can take your pick.'

George couldn't prevent a slight grin. 'In English we call that "Hobson's choice".'

As far as he knew he was the only partisan leader to have been caught and he had a nasty feeling that if the Germans wanted to make an example by shooting someone, he would very likely be that example. Suppressing this thought as he was depressed enough already, he thought of Karen and their meeting on the beach at Montreux. Strange that she was only a few hours away by car. She might just as well be in another world.

The following morning he was called out by a warder and taken along to a small office for questioning. There was a young man behind the desk wearing the badges of a sergeant-major of the S.S.

Once they were alone his curt manner relaxed. 'Sit down, Lieutenant Paterson,' he said in good Italian. 'If you will co-operate and be frank with us, this won't take long and it will certainly help you when you come to trial. Now we know quite a bit about you up to the time that you escaped from San Vittore in July. What happened after that?'

George told a story about living with the partisans, carefully omitting any mention of his visits to Switzerland.

'I decided that my best course was to remain hidden and wait for our armies to arrive,' he concluded.

The idea that the Allied armies would reach North Italy normally sent S.S. officials and other fanatical Nazis into a tearing rage and their usual response was to launch into a tirade as to how Germany was still going to win the war. This man to George's surprise, agreed with him.

He nodded and lowered his voice. 'We can't hope to hold Italy much longer once the ground dries up, and your plan might have worked. Who were the people who sheltered you?'

'I can't remember,' George replied, and both men smiled at the inevitability of the answer.

The S.S. man continued his interrogation for a while, but did not press his questions or make any threats.

Finally George was dismissed feeling rather pleased

about the examination and very thankful there had been no awkward questions about Switzerland.

The days and weeks that followed seemed like an endless period of waiting, wondering what lay in store. Overcrowding made the large cell uncomfortable, but at least they had companionship and he had no trouble settling back into prison routine. The *buiolo* rumours, the rattle of tin cups and plates at mealtime, the jingling of warders' keys, the straw palliasses and the single threadbare blanket were all part of a pattern that had been too painfully familiar for him ever to forget. The food, if anything, was even worse than at San Vittore. The quantity was about the same, but the soup was weaker. However, most of the prisoners came from this area and their families kept them well supplied with parcels of food and cigarettes which the warders, who were not unfriendly, allowed through. These were shared with the lone Canadian whom the young partisans looked up to with considerable respect as one of their leaders. So the poor quality of the rations was not a serious problem.

George, with a lot of time upon his hands to think about his position, decided it was all for the best that neither Karen nor his family knew of his recapture. He must try if he got a chance, to get word to John Birback letting him know exactly what had happened. Also he hoped that John might be able to arrange an escape plan from the outside. But he must warn him to keep word of this from Karen. She had worried enough about his going back to Italy. To learn the Germans had him again would just add to her distress. The problem was, how to get a message out? Not one of his cell-mates had been released, nor was there much hope of it. The Italian warders, though inclined to be friendly, made it quite clear they would do nothing. They would take no risks that might get them into trouble with their German masters. He had been in almost a month and it was Armistice Day before he had his first chance to send word outside.

It was after the evening meal. One of the warders came in to read out a list of names, including a number who had not been partisans at all but merely picked up on suspicion.

'You are being transferred to a labour battalion for war work in Germany,' he told them. 'Be prepared to move tomorrow after breakfast.'

George had in the last weeks become friendly with one of the prisoners, a boy no more than eighteen who had fought with Superbi's Socialist Brigade. This young fellow was an idealist, an ardent patriot who hated with equal intensity both Fascists and Nazis.

'Are you going to let them take you to Germany, Guiseppe?' George asked cautiously.

The young man spat savagely. 'I'll escape from their bloody labour battalion the first night. Then I'll go back into the hills.'

'Do you think you could take a very important letter into Switzerland? The man you hand it to will pay you well.'

'I don't want any pay, Maggiore Giorgio. You give me the letter and tell me where to go and I'll take it.'

Borrowing a piece of paper and a scrap of pencil from Pico, he sat down to write.

Dear John:

Another prison, worse than ever, full of lice and scabies but up to now I'm still in one piece. Narrowly escaped being shot. The danger still exists, but have goodish chance of getting away with it, I think. Here at the moment there is nothing I can do but wait and see what happens. Boring, but at least they don't isolate one in this dump.

If this gets to you, the bearer will be able to give you full details. It was partly my own fault getting caught. Let my natural instinct be overridden by a burst of Italian enthusiasm, and as a result, we arrived 'in bocca al lupo', and got cleaned up. Both Monetta and DiDio dead.

If you can start up anything your end, I'm sure that you will do all you can. Don't tell Karen I've been captured but if the worst happens, then I leave it to you to let her, and my family, know.

George

Holding the piece of paper, young Guiseppe took off his boot and pushed it way up into the toe. 'I'll get it there, never fear,' he assured George after receiving instructions. 'My brother used to bring over cigarettes and I've been across with him.'

Early next day the party left. Their going made a little extra room for the rest and during the next three weeks others were also hauled off for slave labour in the Fatherland. Then one morning George heard his own name called by the turnkey.

'Get your things,' he was ordered. 'You're moving.'

As he had nothing, not even a toothbrush or razor, this didn't take long. Maybe, he thought in sudden hope, they are sending me to a labour battalion. If so, he was pretty certain that he would be able to give them the slip. But this confidence ended when he got outside the cell. Waiting for him, were a couple of tough, burly S.S. men.

'Come with us,' ordered the older man in poor Italian, 'and if you try anything we'll shoot.' He touched his machine-pistol significantly and then, one on either side, they took their prisoner downstairs and out into the courtyard where a car was waiting.

Am I in for a court-martial? he wondered as the vehicle

shot out into the street. He asked the man who had spoken to him, but received only a negative shake of the head. Whether this was in answer to his question or because he didn't understand, George was not certain. However, he was not left long in ignorance. Within a few minutes they drew up at the Novara railroad station where he was ordered out, and with his watchful escort shouting and pushing a way through a crowd of gaping civilians, marched across the platform and aboard a waiting east-bound train.

Milan was in this direction and only twenty-five miles away. It was no great surprise an hour later when they pulled into the well-known station. Another car was waiting for them and they drove quickly through the busy familiar streets where only a year ago he and Roberto Oreste had played hide and seek with the Gestapo as they spirited prisoners away. He wondered what had happened to flamboyant Roberto who had disappeared from his old haunts and hadn't been heard of in months.

Sleet turned the streets and buildings grey and dirty. The route they took through the industrial suburbs confirmed his suspicions as to where they were bound. With a sinking feeling in the pit of his stomach he saw once again as they swung round a corner, the grim, machine-gun studded wall of San Vittore.

Oh, God, another winter of this, he thought gloomily.

CHAPTER NINETEEN

T H E door of the small bare room was flung open and Corporal Franz, squat and brutal looking as ever, swaggered in supported by a couple of Wehrmacht privates and an Italian civilian, the interpreter, who hovered apprehensively on the fringe of the group. A second glance and he realized that it was not Corporal Franz but Sergeant Franz.

God, he thought hopelessly, they've promoted the bastard for kicking people into pulp. Mentally he braced himself for a beating. They would surely put the boots to him in reprisal for the escape. He knew with a feeling of dread that there was no way of escape whether he fought back or was passive. They'd still make one hell of a mess of him. He'd seen it too many times.

He looked the German in the face, trying to appear calm without outward sign of his inward apprehension. Then a strange thing happened. Franz had been surveying him with considerable interest, the filthy clothes, the four days' growth of beard, the unkempt hair and suddenly, without warning, he began to laugh great roaring bellows of merriment that filled the little room with noise. The soldiers and the interpreter, following their chief's lead, commenced to grin and snigger like men who laugh to be polite, though they cannot see a joke.

George himself suddenly reprieved though he knew not why, from the beating that he had anticipated, stared at them open-mouthed with surprise, and this added to Franz's mirth. Finally though, he controlled his laughter to some extent.

'Why,' he spluttered, 'you look as though you've been having a rough time. Guess you've come back here for some kind treatment.'

'Yes, it was rough. Besides, I've missed all of you,' he shot back, playing along with the unexpected good humour.

This brought more laughter. Then Franz became serious, though still friendly.

'Tell me one thing,' he questioned. 'How in the name of God did you manage to escape? We turned the bloody prison upside down, but were never able to figure how you did it.'

George, after a moment's hesitation, decided that part of the truth would hurt no one. Briefly he described the way they had left the ray. Leaving out all reference to the warder and duplicate key, made it appear that they had gone out on chance, and by luck found the door in the outer wall unlocked.

'So, that was it. Well, I'll be damned,' declared the German, his low-browed, rather stupid face clearing at the solution to a problem which had obviously worried him. 'We'll see that you don't get a chance like that again. All right,' he continued, turning to his subordinates, 'put him in the isolation section till I hear what's to be done.'

During the next week he was left to himself, except that the peep-hole slot in the door was frequently opened, both day and night, as the warders checked on him. Obviously they were taking no chances of a second escape. The meals also seemed a little better than he remembered and this was explained in a whisper by the convict orderly who doled out his noonday soup.

'Franz ordered that you're to get an increased ration.'

He couldn't understand this sudden cordiality on the part of the beast, but he was too despondent to care much one way or the other. Most of his thoughts were for Karen, wondering what she would be doing and drawing hope from the thought of their future. All he had to do was stick it out for a few more months until spring when the Allied armies would start rolling north again. There might come another chance at a break and he must keep alert and watchful.

On the morning of the seventh day his door opened to admit a couple of plain-clothes men with hard, unsmiling faces.

Gestapo, he realized instantly, standing up to face them.

'Come with us,' said one crisply, 'and don't try anything.'

Outside he was pushed roughly into a waiting black sedan. The men climbed in on either side and as the doors slammed, the driver edged the vehicle forward, sliding smoothly out through the main gate and into the street beyond.

Am I just being taken for questioning, he wondered uneasily, or is this one of those mock trials the Gestapo sometimes stage for their victims. To distract his thoughts he watched the passers-by and the meagre displays of goods in the store windows. Despite the austerity that war had brought, some shopkeepers were making a rather pathetic attempt at Christmas decorations. He glanced at his coldly impassive guards. Good will towards men didn't go with these boys.

After a short drive they pulled up before a well-known building, the Albergo Regina, and he was quickly hustled inside and led to a room where three men waited.

'Sit down, Lieutenant Paterson,' invited the one who was obviously the chief interrogator. 'We have a few routine questions to ask you.'

He was about thirty, George guessed, fair-haired, a little

thin on top, good looking, yet somehow the face had a bloated unhealthy appearance. The lips were sensual, but it was the eyes, pale blue, cold and expressionless that caught one's attention.

'We would like you to go over your movements after you broke out of San Vittore,' went on this man in a soft effeminate voice. 'Of course we realize that you were helped and we want to know who helped you. Anything you tell us will be quite confidential. If you co-operate with us, things will be much easier for you.'

George launched into the story he had prepared, how he had lived as a hunted fugitive, hiding in the woods, sleeping in barns and sheds, begging or stealing food as best he could until he had thrown in his lot with the partisans. It was a good story, but it didn't impress his listener.

'You're a liar,' shouted the fair-haired man, his voice rising in anger. 'We know you were helped all the way along, and we're going to find out who the traitors are. Either you tell the truth, or you'll end up in front of a firing squad. Now, where did you stay on the night you broke out of prison?'

Stubbornly George stuck to his story that he had been given a lift by an unknown truck driver and had spent the night hidden in a haystack a few miles west of the city.

The other examiners now began to take part in the grilling, firing questions at him demanding names and places and constantly referring back to what he had said previously. They sought to confuse, and so to break down his will to resist. He was deliberately slow in answering, trying to keep his thoughts and story straight. When they cornered him on some point, he would either pretend that he had not understood what they said or, more frequently, that he could not remember an answer, which infuriated his inquisitors.

He was asked if he knew various men and women. He was shown pictures of them, but continued shaking his head which was now aching abominably. Finally, the chief interrogator terminated the interview.

'All right, you lying swine, we'll see you again to-morrow, and if you don't talk then, God help you. Take him away and bring him back at the same time in the morning.'

They led him away, wet with sweat, reeling from nervous exhaustion, yet with a feeling of grim satisfaction. The bastards hadn't managed to get anything out of him, and that was the main thing.

The following day he was grilled again, but he managed to stick to his story. On several occasions they hinted at physical torture but they never resorted to it. At last they gave up and ordered him to be taken away.

'We shall report your lack of co-operation, and you'll very likely be shot as a spy. If you think better of your stupidity and want to save your life by assisting us, you can send word through the prison authorities.'

Back in his cell he felt at a low ebb. The threat might be bluff, but he knew the Gestapo was a law unto itself and every footstep that halted near his cell made him wonder if this was it. They took you to some quiet place and put a pistol to your head. He forced his mind away from such dark, brooding thoughts. If only he could get out of isolation, there might be some faint chance of escape. Maybe John Birback had got his message and was working on it.

He slumped on his bunk, wrapping the blanket round his shoulders. His wrist itched and he rubbed it, then examined the place. It was rough and red. Scabies, he thought disgustedly the prisons were full of it, and he'd seen the rash on other men.

Next morning his hands, wrists and stomach were all inflamed and itching, driving him almost crazy as he struggled against the desire to scratch. When the warder came round during the morning he showed the rash and demanded to see the prison doctor.

'I'll see what I can do,' promised the man, 'but the doctor is always busy and you'll have to wait.'

In late afternoon he was taken to the dispensary where the medical officer, a pleasant young Italian, confirmed his diagnosis.

'So you're a Canadian,' he chatted, applying a cooling solution to the affected places. 'I have a cousin out in Toronto. The last we heard, he was doing well, but of course that was before the war.'

They talked for a time. Conversation of any kind was a relief to George, and he had the feeling that this man was well disposed to him.

'Come back in a couple of days,' he was told finally, 'and we'll see how it's getting along. It may take a week or so to clear up.'

When he returned the doctor was as friendly as ever, again questioning him about Canada while he worked.

'Maybe I shall go there after the war. There's not going to be much future left in poor Italy after the mess these Fascists have made.'

'That's true, Signore Dottore, but at least they won't last much longer. Once spring is here the Allied armies will quickly take Milan, and that will be the end of Mussolini and his gang.'

The other nodded and lowered his voice. 'I suppose you would like to escape?'

'God, yes, in a hurry. The Gestapo is trying to make up its mind whether to shoot me and I'm desperate to get away. Do you think that you could help?'

'It might be possible. I'm not sure. If I could somehow

arrange to get you transferred to the prison infirmary, right by the outer wall there's a gate for ambulances that's practically unguarded. Once you were there, I don't think it would be too difficult for you to get away. The problem, though, is to get you there. Only the most serious cases are admitted, so you've got to appear very sick or I might end up in front of the firing squad.' He laughed a little to conceal his apprehension.

George nodded. 'Naturally I don't want to get you into any trouble. Is there any illness I could fake?'

'Jaundice might be best. I can get some pills that will turn you yellow and you can easily learn the symptoms. If things go well we should be ready to start on the pills by your next visit. Now I think you had better go before anybody starts to get suspicious.'

Returning to his cell his spirits rose with new hope. God willing he might be out in a week, if the Gestapo didn't choose to dispose of him in the meantime. Striding up and down the tiny room he let his imagination play with the future. Soon he would see Karen and they could get married. The thought of holding her in his arms made him frantic with desire and impatient to get out and be on his way.

The doctor was obviously in excellent humour when next he reported.

'Ah, Signore Tenente,' he began immediately they were alone, 'you will be glad to hear that everything goes well. Let me have a look at that rash of yours while I tell you what has happened.

'First I saw an orderly in the infirmary, he's willing to help provided it doesn't get him into trouble and that he gets a couple of hundred thousand lire out of it. Then I saw a friend with the partisans and apparently they know all about you. They'll find the money and hide you until you can cross into Switzerland.'

'That's wonderful. Doctor. I can't tell you how much I appreciate this help. You're probably saving my life.'

The Italian smiled happily. 'Good, good. We're both working for Italy. Now here are the pills. Take three a day and come back in a week. You should be as yellow as a Chinaman then.'

George tucked the packet into an inside pocket and stood up to leave.

'Just a minute,' said the doctor moving to a cupboard and returning with a bottle of liqueur. 'Do you know it's nearly Christmas? We better have a drink to our success.' Reaching for a large tumbler, he filled it with the potent liquor and pushed it across his desk.

'Try this, it's an orange liqueur and very good.'

It was thick and sweet, hot and powerful as it trickled down his throat sending a glow of warmth through his constantly chilled body. The other man gave him a cigarette and for the few minutes he sat there sipping the drink and drawing the biting smoke, he felt content and confident, in a golden haze of optimism.

He would have liked to stay and chat with his new friend, but he realized it might be dangerous for them both.

Locked up once again in isolation he felt his hopes rise. He took one of the pills and sat down to wait for the evening ration of coffee and black bread, occasionally glancing at his skin to see if there was any sign of yellow.

After a week he was once again summoned to the dispensary.

'Let's have a look at you,' said the doctor taking him over to the window for a better light.

George's heart sank as the other, after a careful scrutiny, slowly shook his head.

'No, I'm afraid they haven't done what we hoped. You're yellow, but not yellow enough.'

'Oh blast. What do we do now?'

The doctor frowned. 'Well, I have something else. They are much stronger but dangerous. Have a side effect on some people, but they'll certainly turn you yellow. Are you willing to risk it?'

'Anything to get out of here.'

'All right,' said the doctor counting a number of yellowish pills into an envelope. 'Take eight of these a day and I'll see you again in four days. This time it's got to work because those scabies of yours are practically healed and the warders will be getting suspicious.'

The new pills made him feel somewhat groggy, but they were certainly effective in changing his skin colour. He wondered just how far advanced were the plans for the actual escape. Maybe everything was arranged and waiting and he would get away tomorrow night. The mere possibility made him feel good.

Heavy boots halted by his cell. The bolt rattled and the door swung open. He got up from the bunk, heart pounding, and for a moment there was a feeling of despair, even panic.

A man in uniform swaggered in. Almost with relief he saw it was Sergeant Franz.

Thumbs tucked into belt, Franz surveyed him. 'Well, I've got good news for you, Herr Paterson. The Gestapo are through with you and you're being transferred to the Wehrmacht wing to await court-martial.'

He sounded relieved. Suddenly George realized why he had received better treatment and better rations than previously. The Allies were getting closer and even a doltish brute like Franz could see the way the wind was blowing and did not want his death to be laid at his door.

This news shook him badly. This would completely ruin the escape. The German army kept one wing for its own military defaulters. It had its own commandant, a captain, its own administrative staff, even its own doctor. That the move should come just now, when escape was so close, was cruel. He felt like smashing in Franz's ugly face to relieve his feelings, but refrained from this folly and nodded his acceptance of the transfer order.

CHAPTER TWENTY

THE Wehrmacht wing was an almost exact duplicate of the political rays, but conditions inside were somewhat better. The German doctor, a young cadet, gave him only the most cursory of examinations.

'Malaria,' he decided without much interest, indicating the yellowed skin.

George nodded and the other, without further comment, looked down his throat, tapped his chest and ordered the guard to take him away.

The wing was filled with German army personnel, though he quickly realized they were by no means all Germans. They included volunteers or reluctant conscripts from almost every country in Eastern Europe. All were here for serious military crimes—desertion, cowardice, rape and robbery were but a few of the charges. He was given a cell on the ground floor and had the limited degree of daytime freedom allowed all prisoners.

A young Yugoslav, a boy about eighteen, was in an adjoining cell and George got to like him. He was well educated, spoke several languages and after unwilling conscription into the Wehrmacht, had deserted, only to be recaptured and sent to San Vittore. He had been sentenced to death and now awaited execution with considerable stoicism and courage. Those who had been condemned were not told when the sentence would be carried out. The first indication they had was the early morning arrival of the execution squad. These pre-dawn visits occurred on an average about once or twice a week and afterwards one of the work parties would have the depressing job of cleaning up the cell, knowing that its occupant had been alive only a few hours ago.

On the other side was a German major, a lean hawk-nosed man of about thirty-five who had fought in France, Russia and North Africa. He had been decorated for gallantry several times and now was imprisoned, charged with homosexuality. He was coldly intelligent, and the two would become involved in a lively discussion on the conduct of the war.

Because of his rank and his proven courage, the German guards treated him with respect. He was thus able to find out and keep his fellow prisoners posted on the latest developments along the battle front, developments which usually brought comfort to the Canadian, if to none of the others.

Food was in terribly short supply and George became gaunt, with sunken cheeks and protruding bones, suffering from lassitude, the result of a near-starvation diet. Physical training was a nightmare, dreaded by all. German army warders, unlike Franz and his S.S. thugs in the other rays, were by and large a decent group, mostly older men who did their job without excess of brutality. There was one, however, a beefy sergeant-major, who gave them physical training and who was as sadistic, in his way, as any Gestapo torturer. He delighted in forcing weak, emaciated men to do hard physical exercises until they collapsed from exhaustion.

George, more powerfully built and stronger than most of his fellows, never passed out, but each day his hatred of this red-faced tormentor grew.

'God, just let me get my hands on this bastard after the war,' he prayed, adding him to a list that was headed by Franz and Swartz.

The cold that winter was intense, and every night he would wake many times, shivering under the one miserably thin blanket. Waking like this very early one morning after he had been there a number of weeks, he heard the ominous ring of steel-shod boots, as a squad of men marched in from the central rotunda. The death squad, he thought with a sinking feeling; another poor devil is for it.

Just outside his cell, he heard a low command and they came to a halt.

Suddenly the dread thought struck like a sledge-hammer. Was this to be the end of everything? Karen—he almost cried out at the unbearable thought of never again holding her.

There was a low-toned conversation outside and he stood up, determined to face them calmly. Then he heard a foot-step, the turn of a key in a lock and a door swung open. It was not his. He realized, with a wild surge of relief that made him tremble and almost collapse on the bunk, that they had come for young Peter next door. Thankfulness turned to horror when he realized the penalty this boy had to pay as a victim of war.

There were a few minutes of silence. Then footsteps, a quiet order, and the squad moved off, silent except for the thud of their retreating footsteps. Later that day he had to clean out the bare, cold cell that had been Peter's last home.

The weeks dragged by. February passed, then March, and each day brought a new crop of *buiolo* rumours. The Germans were advancing on the Eastern Front, on the Western Front. Montgomery was striking deep into the Fatherland, a new secret weapon had been launched. Hitler was dead. Churchill was dead. The German generals were trying to arrange a surrender. There were almost as many rumours as there were prisoners, but George, trying to sort out the wheat from the chaff, was fairly certain the war was dragging to a final and successful conclusion.

Actual confirmation of this came one day while they were in the courtyard doing physical training. It was the latter part of April. Suddenly they heard it: a faint distant rattle—small-arms fire.

The following morning inside the cells, they could hear far away the sporadic crack of rifles and machine-guns, very faint but unmistakable. To George, who had slept little the previous night, the sound was like a message of hope. If the partisans were rising in Milan the Allies could not be far distant.

Later in the day new orders arrived. All prisoners in the building were to be concentrated in the cells on the second floor and George found himself packed into a tiny cell with the Major, an Austrian second lieutenant charged with desertion and three other ranks, a burly paratrooper, a Rumanian and an alert little Hungarian who reminded him of a bright-eyed sparrow.

'I wonder what all this means,' he asked.

'I know,' responded the Major, in obvious gloom. 'All the political prisoners are being evacuated to Germany.'

George groaned, his hope of liberation beginning to fade.

'Look here, Major, we've got to do something. If we want to escape, now's the time.'

The German officer nodded and they fell to discussing possibilities. They talked in whispers until late in the night, by which time a plan of sorts had evolved.

'Well, it may work, and it's better than just sitting here on our arses until they herd us off like cattle.'

Morning brought none of the usual noises. They could hear activity outside, but no doors opened to herald the arrival of coffee and bread. This worried them, for it was not only hunger that caused concern. Their whole plan of escape, if it was to succeed, hinged on the arrival of the rations.

They sat about, tense and waiting. With each passing minute it seemed more certain that something else had gone wrong. At last, however, they heard the rattle of the handcart that brought round the food.

It stopped by their cell. Keys rattled, and the heavy door swung open to admit two orderlies, prisoners like themselves, who doled out the rations. Outside, leaning against the metal gallery railing that looked down on the main floor, was the guard paying little or no attention to the distribution of food inside the cell. While George and the burly paratrooper stood near the entrance to block the man's view, the Major beckoned the orderlies to him and in a quick whisper told them of the plan for escape and their part in it. They were surprised, but quickly grasped what was wanted of them.

'Ya, Herr Major,' nodded the younger. 'We will do it. Anything to get out of this hell-hole.'

The door slammed behind them, they heard the lock turn and the cart move along. It would take some time to issue the rations, so they took the opportunity to munch the coarse black bread.

The plan they had decided upon called for the orderlies to warn all prisoners to be ready, and when they reached the last cell, almost directly across from their own, they and the inmates of that cell were to overpower the guard, grab his keys and run back along the catwalk opening all the doors. Meanwhile, all the other prisoners, as soon as they heard the scuffle and shout, were to create pandemonium so that the noise would deafen and confuse the soldiers downstairs long enough for all the cells to be emptied. After that the plans were vague, but there was a door, normally kept locked, at the far end of the building which led directly out to one of the gates in the outer wall, and if they could only force the guards to open this, they would be away.

George quietly moved over to the door to listen by the Judas slot. He could faintly hear the cart and judged it about halfway down the far side. There would be a few minutes yet. He stood waiting, straining his ears, tense for the moment of action. Finally, when he could not stand another moment of suspense, the signal came.

'All right, fellows, let's make noise,' he ordered, kicking and hammering on the door with his fists, yelling at the top of his voice.

The others immediately joined in and he heard them tearing the bunks off the wall. In a moment they were using them as rams to pound on the heavy door panels, shrieking and yelling like demented men, while throughout the building they could hear a great and growing volume of sound, a mighty roar of anger and defiance. They kept it up, minute after minute unaware, because of the tumult, of what was happening outside. The only noise that would have cut through that din was the sharp crack of rifle or machine-gun fire, and they heard none of that.

'Keep it up, you buggers,' George shouted hoarsely, noticing that the Rumanian and the Austrian were flagging.

At last their lock turned. The door was shoved open and they poured out on to the gallery. It was bedlam with the noise coming at them in a continuous torrent of sound. Three or four hundred prisoners had rushed on to the main floor, a shouting, screaming, raging mob that every moment was working itself into a greater frenzy. At the end, behind sandbags, two machine-gunners supported by other soldiers who had just run in from the rotunda, watched the riot in bewildered stupefaction. Obviously they were stunned by the suddenness of the break, confused by the noise, unwilling to fire on fellow soldiers and also aware that if they fired they would probably be torn to pieces by the berserk mob.

George started for one of the steel staircases to take his place with the others, but the Major caught his arm and shouted something. It was lost in the uproar. Seeing this, he cupped his hands and bellowed.

'Don't be a fool. Stay here where we can see what's happening. No point in being shot down if they open fire.'

This made sense. Why should he die for a gang of Germans, men who were his enemies. He stood by the rail and watched the frightening scene below.

For ten minutes they waited as the uproar from the crowd grew in intensity while no one, guards or prisoners, was certain what to do. Then George, to break the impasse, shouted a suggestion to the Major who nodded and beckoned the Hungarian. 'Go down there,' he ordered pointing to the sandbags, 'and tell that sergeant that if he doesn't open the outside door, we'll attack, and they will all be torn to bits.'

The man was obviously unhappy with the assignment, but his sense of discipline was strong. Clicking his heels, he clattered down the nearest staircase and out into the open area of floor between the rioting mob and the frightened soldiers. Putting up his hands, he advanced towards the machine-gun while behind him the clamour slowly died down as all watched this new development. The sergeant came forward and the two of them spoke, the Hungarian arguing vehemently while the other feebly protested. As they watched, the sergeant gave up, shrugged his shoulders and, reaching into his pocket, pulled out a key. Waving this above his head like a flag of truce, he advanced towards the now silent mob.

They parted to let him through, every eye on him as he walked the length of the ray to the steel door that led to freedom. He fumbled as he inserted the key into the lock, and then the door swung open, letting in a shaft of morning sunlight. A roar of triumph broke out, then the whole surging mass stampeded towards the opening.

'Come on,' shouted George, 'let's go.'

They joined the tidal wave of humanity that surged through the doorway and out past the gate into the streets of Milan. There was no shooting from the outer wall. Presumably the Fascist guards were taking no action to provoke this angry mob.

'I'm free, I'm free,' he kept repeating as he turned for an instant to glance back at the grim walls of San Vittore. Knowing it would not be long before the S.S. would be combing the streets, he started to run.

CHAPTER TWENTY-ONE

THERE was excitement in the street. Shifting, restless groups of people armed with rifles or pistols, talking, laughing, singing and occasionally there were shouts of 'Down with the Fascists' 'Long Live Italy'. The Milan partisans had risen. Had they seized control of the entire city, or just this area? He questioned several men, but they obviously knew no more than the local situation.

'There was a great battle yesterday,' one of them proudly told him, 'down by that street corner. Then the Germans went off and they haven't shown their noses back here, but I don't know what has happened in other districts. Maybe our captain would know. He's down at the wine shop.'

George didn't bother to pursue enquiries further. He still carried a lingering fear of pursuit, and though the partisans seemed to be pretty much in control, there was still the sound of distant firing. It might be a German counter-attack and he didn't want to get caught up in that. Pushing his way through the celebrating crowd, he walked quickly, beginning to sweat profusely as the morning heat increased. An occasional tram rattled by, but there wasn't a single lira in his pocket and he was too newly out of prison to want to draw attention by not paying.

After an hour of hard walking, he reached his destination and knocked. There was much talk and laughter inside, and he had to rap again before he was heard. Then the door opened. A woman looked up at him in amazement.

'Giorgio, Giorgio, where have you been this time?'

'Maria,' he grinned, 'you look more beautiful than ever.'

Maria Resta laughed delightedly, flung her arms about his neck and kissed him soundly.

'Come in. We're celebrating.'

The Resta family, brothers, sisters, uncles, aunts, cousins, were squeezed into the tiny living-room. They were drinking and discussing the great events of the past few days and George was introduced and honoured as one of the heroes of the resistance. Maria demanded his story.

'That's strange,' she said when he told of his return to San Vittore. 'They had me in for a couple of months on suspicion, but I had no idea you were there. Thought you had got back to England.'

'No such luck, my dear. I was beginning to feel like their star boarder. But it's practically over now, and as soon as it is I'm heading back to Switzerland.'

They talked for a long time, both finding it hard to realize that the long years of fear and danger, the years when they had lived in the shadows were coming to an end. About them, Maria's friends and relatives talked and sang, drank and ate with Italian gusto, savouring the satisfaction of being able to shout 'To hell with Mussolini!'

It was late into the night before George stretched out on the couch exhausted. He slept soundly, not bothered by the snores of an uncle in the armchair.

When he awoke Maria and her husband were still asleep in the bedroom and he didn't want to disturb them, so he got up quietly and went out, feeling much better in the clean morning air. There was a little restaurant across the street where he had eaten on previous visits. The proprietor and his son, an auxiliary policeman, were sympathetic to the partisans and had known that he was a fugitive from the Germans.

They remembered him and were warm in their welcome, especially when he identified himself as a Canadian officer.

'This is wonderful, Signore Tenente,' exclaimed Renato, the son. 'You must come with me and meet Bocci, our new Chief of Police. We have cleared out the Fascists and he has taken over. I know that he will want to thank you for your work for Italy.'

George was eager to find out exactly what was going on and police headquarters would be a good place to begin his enquiries. He set off with Renato who was in uniform ready to go on duty.

They were ushered into the Chief's office and when Bocci, who had been a junior officer until yesterday, heard Renato's enthusiastic introduction, he was most cordial, ready to give information and assistance.

'What you need,' he finally decided after they had talked for a while, 'is a car. I'll put one at your disposal and you'd better have an escort. There are some Fascist gangsters still on the loose and quite a bit of shooting going on. Renato, get another man, and accompany Signore Tenente for as long as he needs.'

They spent the rest of the day touring the city. Everywhere the populace was celebrating the uprising by cheering, singing and dancing. George, still in Alpine clothing, driven about in a big limousine by a couple of respectful young police officers, was taken for some important partisan chieftain just out of the hills and given a rousing reception. There was enough wine offered to put him out of action for a week, but he wisely decided to refuse. As far as he could judge, the larger part of Milan was now liberated. Only a few strong points, such as the German army and the S.S. Headquarters and the streets around them were still in enemy hands. The prefecture was also held by diehard Fascists and it was believed that Mussolini was there.

There was still a considerable amount of private shooting going on. A number of Fascists were hunted down and given short shift by the partisans. Many innocent people were also being murdered by enemies who took advantage of the confusion and the general hysteria to settle old grudges. Confusion and uncertainty spread everywhere and so did the partisans. A week before, there were no more than one or two thousand in all of Milan, devoted men and women who had waged a long, dangerous and uphill battle against the régime. But now the great bulk of the population, including those who had previously remained neutral, as well as the out-and-out Fascists, rushed to sign up as members of the resistance.

The following morning there was to be a great victory parade. Renato and the other policeman, Pepe, drove George to a vantage point along the route. After the usual wait the procession came in sight, trucks from the surrounding countryside jammed with partisans, marching units that made up in enthusiasm what they lacked in drill, impromptu bands, all led by a shiny black open touring car formerly used by Fascist officials. There was a man standing in the rear of this vehicle waving to the crowds and, as he came closer, George suddenly recognized him. 'Well, I'll be damned, it's Moscatelli.'

The Communist brigadier saw him at almost the same instant and shouting to his driver to stop, jumped out and rushed over; his usually surly face relaxed into a broad grin.

'Maggiore Giorgio,' he beamed, shaking hands enthusiastically, 'I thought the worms had you months ago. This is a surprise, and on such a great day for Italy. Come along, you've got to ride with me. You should be in the parade. I want to hear your story.'

Amused, half reluctant, George was pulled into the car and standing beside Moscatelli they drove through the wildly cheering crowds, all the while waving, catching flowers and throwing kisses to girls.

It was an exhilarating feeling, this wild public adoration. When they reached the Piazza del Duomo the roar that went up from the massed crowd was like nothing he had ever heard before.

The leaders mounted the steps of the cathedral. There were to be speeches. Moscatelli was first to the microphone.

George, standing behind, listened for a while. The man spoke powerfully, with fire, but went on much too long until finally George slipped away.

'I've just heard a rumour,' Renato told him when he got back to the car, 'that some Allied planes have landed at the airport. Would the Signore like to drive out and see?'

The rumour turned out to be correct. Half a dozen Grasshoppers, tiny one-man observation planes, stood alone on the runway at the bare, deserted airport, while near them a small crowd talked excitedly. As he approached, George could see several men in khaki uniforms right in the centre of the group, and pushing his way through, came face to face with a young American second lieutenant.

'Hello,' he greeted in English. 'I'm an escaped P.O.W. Been working with the underground here and I'm damned glad to see you fellows.'

They clustered around him, the young officer and five sergeants, all curious and eager to exchange news.

'Ah reckon the army'll be here in four or five days,' one of the sergeants told him. 'We were sent up to see what is going on.'

He spent the afternoon with these new friends, giving them what information he had about Milan and the surrounding countryside, enjoying the sensation of talking freely once again in his native tongue. When the young officer radioed his report he got George to come out with him to the set in case they wanted any background information.

'You'd better have some chow with us,' he said when they went off the air. 'Looks as if the Krauts didn't over-feed you.'

It was the best meal in months. Steaks fried over a port-able cooker, white bread, real coffee with sugar and tinned milk, peaches that he swore came from his native Okana-gan, followed by whiskey with which the Americans were well supplied.

After he had waved the airmen off next morning, he de-cided to drive up to Como. He had tried on the preceding day to phone Karen just to hear her voice and say how much he loved her, but the exchanges were in complete confusion. No calls were going out of the city.

It was a lovely morning. Lake Como was blue and the town appeared gay in the spring sunshine, but here again his luck was no better. Apparently no calls were going across the frontier.

Maybe I could get across, he thought, but at the border he found the Swiss guards polite, but firm.

'No, Signore, we are sorry, but no one is being admitted without special permission from Berne.'

Disappointed, he returned to Como where the uniform of his police escort procured them a good lunch at a local restaurant. Afterwards they returned to Milan.

We'll call in at police headquarters, George decided, and see if Bocci has any news. News, as opposed to rumour, was everyone's goal.

Bocci did have news. 'Some of your paratroopers landed at the airport this morning commanded by a Colonello Vincent. They have taken over Pavolini's villa as their headquarters.'

George knew the name of Pavolini. He was infamous as one of Mussolini's chief henchmen.

'Do you know where the villa is?' he asked Renato and

at the other's nod, hurriedly thanked Bocci, eager now to join up with his own people.

The villa was a mansion set amid beautifully kept lawns with swimming pool and tennis courts. By the imposing front door a private in khaki battledress stood on guard.

'I'm an escaped British officer,' he told the man who eyed him in some surprise but quickly snapped smartly to attention. 'Where's your C.O.?'

'Colonel Vincent is in the first room on the left, sir.'

'What unit is this, anyway?'

'No. 1 Special Force, sir.'

This was a real piece of luck. No. 1 Special Force was his own unit. Telling Renato to wait, he went into the ornate, marble-floored reception hall and tapped on the door.

'Come in,' came the curt invitation.

A man in uniform was sitting behind the big desk, writing furiously. He wrote on, finishing a sentence before looking up.

'Lieutenant George Paterson, sir. I was working for the S.O.E. out of Switzerland.' He told his story briefly while the other listened almost impatient at the interruptions.

'Very well, Paterson,' he said briskly when the younger man had finished. 'The first thing you had better do is get spruced up. For God's sake get into some clean clothes. I'll talk to you later.'

The Colonel's disinterest and coolness irritated George. The Alpine clothes were filthy, but they had gone through a lot and since his escape he hadn't been able to find anything better that would fit. Surely after what he had been through, it wasn't asking too much to expect a friendly reception?

'Yes, sir,' he replied formally, and stalking out of the house, he got into his car and slammed the door saying, 'Let's get the hell out of here, Renato.'

Later he was to find Colonel Vincent not only an excel-

lent officer but also a warm and loyal friend. His pre-
occupation and briskness during their meeting was due to
the pressure and urgency of the many decisions that he was
being called upon to make. But at this moment, George
felt intensely annoyed by what seemed to him cavalier
treatment.

'Where to, Signore?' asked Renato timidly.

George, fuming and in a thoroughly bad mood, had an
idea. He had heard that the partisans had taken over San
Vittore, and he had one or two scores to settle down there.

'Drive me to the prison,' he ordered. 'There's someone I
want to see.'

The resistance captain now in control greeted him with
great respect, both as an allied officer and as a man who
had twice managed to escape from the fortress, but he
laughed when George asked to see Sergeant Franz.

'He must have been a popular one, that Franz. I've had
a dozen here, all wanting to get their hands on him, but he
was gone when we took over. That kind of rat always has
an escape hole. Come along though, and I'll show you what
we do have in the bag.'

The score of dirty, unshaven Germans were a sorry-looking bunch. There were also some of the Italian warders who
had been accused of excessive brutality to the inmates. He
looked them over briefly, without much interest since
Franz was not among them. Then he saw a face that
brought back bitter memories. It was the beefy, red-faced
sergeant-major who had taken such a sadistic delight in
giving the prisoners physical training until they dropped
from sheer exhaustion.

'Here you,' he snapped, beckoning the frightened man
whose ruddy cheeks had turned a dirty grey. 'Now
we'll give you a little training so you know what it feels
like.'

For half an hour, while the partisans looked on with delight, he put the bully through some of the toughest exercises until finally soaked with sweat he had reached the point of collapse.

'All right, you bastard, you can break off now. I just hope some of the others come back to give you more of the treatment.'

Late next morning he felt he had better report to Pavolini's villa. This time he met a dark, grey-haired man in civilian clothes who introduced himself as Colonel Salvadori.

'Sit down. Let me give you a drink. The house boasts an excellent cellar,' said the stranger.

Salvadori, he discovered from their conversation, was a British officer of Italian descent, who had been working with the resistance in Milan for many months, though George had not previously known of his existence.

'I've heard all about you though, Paterson. In fact, we had five million lire available for anyone who could spring you out of San Vittore. We were behind the doctor when he tried at Christmas with the plan that unfortunately fell through.'

George was gratified to learn that his people had been trying to get him out and the two men talked for some time.

'Now I suppose you would like to get cleaned up and into some fresh clothes before you meet the others at lunch?' He rang a bell and an Italian servant came in. 'We've inherited most of Pavolini's retainers,' he explained.

'This is Lieutenant Paterson,' he told the man. 'Give him the best bedroom in the house and find him clean clothes.'

George followed the servant up a magnificent marble staircase and along a panelled, high-ceilinged corridor to a room that took his breath away. It was vast, with carpets that were soft and deep, walls covered with crimson silk and a crystal chandelier that would have graced a palace; the bed and the furnishings were king-size.

'This is Pavolini's room,' whispered the man, sounding a little frightened at the idea of introducing a roughly dressed stranger to the great man's chamber. 'The bathroom is through here.'

About the size of a small home, it was finished in black marble with the tub like a small swimming pool sunk into the floor. George turned on one of the taps experimentally and whistled in surprise. Unlike most Italian plumbing, this tap gushed hot water.

When George had had a shave and a long soaking, the servant came back.

'I've laid out fresh clothing, Signore, and I've found a grey suit and some shoes which I think will fit.'

Feeling sharper and better dressed than he had in months, George answered the summons of a distant gong and appeared for lunch in the cool and spacious dining-room. There were six officers, Vincent, Salvadori and four younger paratroopers to whom he was introduced.

'We're a very small family,' explained Vincent affably. 'There are only ten all told in our party. Sit here and tell us your story again. I was too busy yesterday to take it all in.'

The meal was good and well served, and it was singularly pleasing to be among his own people again. When cigarettes and coffee arrived, he judged it a propitious moment to ask for leave.

'My fiancée is at Montreux in Switzerland,' he told Vincent, 'and I haven't been able to get word to her since I was captured. Do you think I could get a few days' leave and permission to cross the border?'

'I'd gladly give you leave, George. You've certainly earned it, but I couldn't get you across. I understand the

Swiss aren't letting anyone through without special permission. Once the army is here, perhaps in three or four days, I may be able to arrange something. Until then I'm afraid it's no go.'

The younger man nodded gloomily, well aware how tight the frontier was shut.

'Just relax and take it easy for the next few days,' continued the Colonel. 'You've got friends here. Have a good time and I promise to do what I can.'

Despite a burning impatience to see Karen he had to be content with this. Thanking Vincent, George went up to his room to try out that luxurious bed and do a little quiet reading. The hectic pace of the last few days, coming after his stay in San Vittore, was beginning to tell. He had also promised to take Peter Williams, the youngest of the paratroop officers, out that evening to show him Milan and he had a feeling, a very strong feeling, that it was going to be a wild, late night.

The bed was all he had anticipated and for a while he read, but without much interest. Then it seemed to him that he was in a very large room, it must have been a ballroom, in which people were laughing and talking, while in the centre couples were dancing to the music of an orchestra that was playing in the background. Suddenly, across the room he saw Karen, slim and lovely in a white dress, smiling a little secret smile as she listened to the music.

He tried to call. All that came was a hoarse, croaking whisper that was lost in the talk about him, while his feet, though he tried desperately to move, were held by invisible clamps to the floor. At that moment an alarm bell clanged. Though he could not be sure why, he knew as did all the others, that it was a warning of some dread happening. They all began to leave the room and he watched in agony, unable to move, as Karen joined the others and dis-

appeared from his sight through one of the doors. The bell
kept on and on, sounding its warning as he fought to free
himself.

With a start he was awake. Years of danger and uncertainty had trained him to come instantly from sleep to
full alert. The bell rang again and he realized that it came
from a small bedside phone. The sun, he noticed, as he
swung his feet to the floor, was coming full in the western
windows. He must have been out for hours.

Picking up the receiver he said '*Pronto.*'

From the other end came a voice that was both impatient and imperative. 'Get Pavolini on the line and
hurry.'

George was startled. Didn't the man know the British
were here? And—that voice—where had he heard it
before?

'Pavolini?' he questioned, to gain time.

'Yes, and hurry, you fool.'

Then it came to him. This was a voice he had heard on
countless radio broadcasts. He was certain now who the
caller was.

'One moment, your Excellency, and I will get him,' he
replied, and putting down the receiver dashed down the
great staircase and into Vincent's office.

'Sir,' he shouted as the Colonel looked up startled from
his work. 'I'm certain I've got Mussolini on the phone.'

Only a few words of explanation were needed and then
both men were sprinting upstairs, neither quite sure how
to take advantage of the opportunity. 'Tell him Pavolini
has been sent for and try to keep him talking,' ordered
Vincent.

George picked up the receiver. 'Ullo.' There was no
answer. '*Mi sentite?* Do you hear me?' Still no answer. The
line was dead.

'Oh, blast,' he swore, shaking the phone after vainly trying a number of times, 'he must have got suspicious and rung off.'

They looked at each other, wondering. Had they just missed a historic chance? Could they have persuaded him to surrender to them? Would it have made any difference? Would it have shortened the war by a single day if they had?

Next day Bocci, who was in contact with Vincent, gave them hard news. On the preceding afternoon Mussolini had left the prefecture and gone to Cardinal Schuster's palace to confer with Cadorna, Marazza and Lombardi, high officers in the Committee of National Liberation about surrender. Then in the evening after his return, he had suddenly left Milan with a small convoy of cars and trucks, accompanied by his mistress Claretta Petacci, and a number of Fascist dignitaries. Amid the excitement and confusion, they had sped through the streets unchecked. No one was certain where they were bound. Some thought Switzerland, others Germany, while there was a rumour Pavolini was still somewhere in the city, gathering together a force of three or four thousand die-hard Blackshirts who were to join their Duce somewhere in the mountains for a last-ditch stand.

'I'd be willing to bet that all the die-hard Blackshirts have joined the partisans,' George commented when Vincent told him this.

With no duties to keep him occupied, with a car which he had prudently kept, together with his obliging police escort, George spent the next few days very pleasantly celebrating with old friends, making countless new ones and everywhere being fêted as a hero of the resistance. It would have been fun if only Karen had been there and their future clear.

Returning to the villa one afternoon he decided to write her. God knew when he would get permission to cross the border, but maybe he could find someone to smuggle a letter through and mail it on the other side.

There was a writing-desk with paper in his room and just as he sat down there was a knock and Vincent came in.

'George, I was speaking to a friend of yours this afternoon—John Birback from Locarno. He was given permission to cross and came down with the American Vice-Consul. He wants to see you. They're going to a party this evening at a friend's house and he would like you to meet him there. Here's the address.'

George was trembling with excitement. John would have a message from Karen. Perhaps he could arrange a crossing.

The party was in full swing when he arrived. It was a big house crowded with revellers whose talk and laughter almost drowned the electric gramophone and its canned dance music. He stood for a moment or two watching, not seeing anyone he knew, but then a man came up, introduced himself and took him over to meet some of the others.

It was while they were talking that he spotted Birback, sitting in a little alcove off the main room, deep in conversation with an elderly grey-haired man. It was some time before he was able to break away from a very patriotic young matron and cross over to join them.

'George, it's good to see you,' said Birback warmly. 'This is Cyrus Carter, my opposite number with the Americans.'

They shook hands and Carter, shrewd yet friendly, questioned him about the happenings of the last few days. He answered as briefly as he could with courtesy, but his thoughts were elsewhere, and at the first opportunity he turned back to Birback.

'How's Karen?' he enquired, trying to keep his tone casual. 'Have you had any word from her?'

The assistant consul shifted in his chair and looked down. 'I've been awfully busy, George,' he muttered, 'no chance to get in touch with anybody.'

'But she's sent a message for me, hasn't she?' he persisted.

There was an awkward silence, then Birback turned, almost desperately to Carter. 'For Christ's sake, Cyrus,' he begged, 'you know Karen. Tell him.'

There was an ominous pause. Then in a quiet tone like a man hating what he must say, the grey-haired American began.

'I've got some bad news for you, George. Karen and her family are old friends of mine and when she heard that I was coming down to Milan she asked me to find you and bring you a message.

'You've got to remember that she's very young and for months she didn't know whether you were dead or alive. She met someone else—someone she had known before.' There was silence as he searched for the right words... 'Well ... to put it bluntly she asked me to tell you she feels you both made a mistake by rushing into an engagement. Now she wants to marry this other man. She hopes you'll understand and won't think too badly of her.'

George stood there, fighting to control his emotions. Carter continued:

'Believe me, she's a nice girl and sorry about hurting you, but that's the way it is. Guess you might call it another war casualty.'

George was stunned, unbelieving, like a healthy man who is suddenly told he is about to die. It couldn't be true. Karen loved him. There must be some mistake. Then he looked into Carter's kindly eyes and knew it was true. There was no mistake.

'Thank you,' he said quietly, unemotionally striving to

keep his face a mask. 'I suppose these things just happen and you can't do much about it.'

Birback, who had slipped away, now returned with a very stiff drink. 'Here,' he said awkwardly, 'get this into you. It'll help.'

After a while they left, realizing he wanted to be alone. Occasionally others came over, but he scarcely noticed them and his moody silence discouraged all attempts at friendship. Karen in love with someone else. Never to see her again. His world after all the struggle and privation, had crumbled. The future was bleak. There was no anger, just dull, hopeless despair. Why did it have to happen this way, he kept thinking, knowing all the time there was no real answer.

He tried to get drunk and forget her, but he couldn't. The party went on around his island of despair increasing in noise. Sometime towards dawn he fell into a restless sleep that brought relief from the bitter pain of reality.

When he awoke the day was well established yet there were still people in the big room, those who could not face the thought of going home, dead-eyed people who drank and talked and smoked without enthusiasm, killing time until the next party. He felt, as he rubbed heavy eyes and licked dry lips that he was one of them, the lost souls caught in the backwater of war.

Renato, still trim and smart in his uniform, was in deep conversation with a young woman, but he came over. Standing up as the young policeman approached, he whispered, 'Let's get the hell out of here,' and he strode out into the warm April sunlight.

'Where to?' enquired Renato as they got into the car, waking Pepe who had been asleep on the back seat.

'Anywhere you want.'

They drove for a time in silence. The streets were busy and as they approached the Square of the Fifteen Martyrs, renamed in honour of a group of partisans who had been shot there a few months previously, they saw it was filled with a surging cheering crowd that milled and pushed around an open space in its centre.

'I wonder what the hell's going on there?' muttered Renato. 'Should we go and see?'

'May as well,' said George without curiosity.

With his policemen on either side forming a wedge, he pushed through the excited throng which, seeing the uniforms, parted to give him passage. 'They're like people at a carnival,' he thought, 'out for a day's amusement.'

They forced through the increasingly tight-packed mass, and finally broke into the open space at the centre.

'My God,' gasped George in sudden horror.

The pavement in front of him was like the floor of a slaughter-house, littered with corpses piled indiscriminately where they had been tossed. He counted them 'thirteen, fourteen, fifteen, sixteen, seventeen', and one was a woman, young and beautiful, who lay with her eyes wide open, eyes that had once been dark and lustrous, but now stared blankly into the sun.

'That's his mistress,' snarled a woman beside him, 'the whore.'

He did not reply but the words started a bitter thought. She at least, had been loyal to the end.

At his feet lay a body, that of a heavy-jowled elderly man, his face mottled grey and slack-jawed in death, and with his head, which had been crushed on one side by a heavy blow, lying across the woman's breast. There was no need to ask the name of this corpse. It was Benito Mussolini at the end of his trail.

'The partisans caught them trying to escape and shot them yesterday,' continued the woman beside him with obvious relish.

He looked down at the broken thing that had been the

Duce. This was the symbol and the architect of all that they had fought against for so long. He should be wildly triumphant like all these others, but there was no triumph, no elation in him, only a feeling of sick emptiness.

'String them up,' yelled a voice from somewhere behind. 'String them up so that we can all see.'

He turned and began to force his way back, out of the crowd.

EPILOGUE

FOR his work with the Resistance, George Paterson was promoted captain and awarded the Military Cross with two bars. In addition, he was made a Freeman of the City of Milan, an honour seldom bestowed on foreigners.

Despite this recognition he was at a low ebb, extremely despondent over Karen's change of heart. Soon after peace came to Europe, he volunteered for service in the Pacific, but was asked by the British Government, because of his knowledge of conditions, to stay on in Italy and assist the Allied authorities in the post-war period.

He remained in Milan more than a year. The job completed and time having healed his hurt, he returned to university in Edinburgh to work for his B.Sc. degree in forestry.

After graduation, still eager for adventure, he took a government post in Tanganyika. It was here, some months later, that he met 'Oojie' Stroudley, newly arrived from England, who quickly dispelled for him the last lingering memories of Karen.

They were married in 1949. After a number of years in East Africa, George brought his family, Oojie and their two children, Theresa and Allan, home to Canada.

Today they live in Vancouver where he continues his profession as partner in a firm of forest management consultants, a job that takes him to many parts of the world.

Those who have read the book *Return Ticket* by Lieutenant-Colonel Anthony Deane-Drummond, which describes this officer's part in the original paratroop raid and his subsequent escape to England, will notice that George is referred to as Pat Paterson. This was an army nickname but, as it was not used during his years with the partisans, I have avoided confusion by giving him his proper Christian name throughout.

Rossi, whose real name is Nino Bacciagaluppi, refused any reward for the work he and his organization did in helping almost three thousand escaping prisoners of war to get across the border into Switzerland. But after the liberation he was presented by the Allies with a gold cigarette case, suitably inscribed in recognition of his outstanding service. Today he still lives and works in the Milan area, as does Maria Resta, who was such a loyal comrade throughout the long struggle.

The Riccinis, where Paterson had his headquarters while working in the Brescia area, were held in prison for several months but were eventually released for lack of evidence against them. Gabi remained safely hidden by her Milan relatives and after the war met and married an American serviceman.

While Roberto Oreste's movements after George's recapture are not clear, it is known that he was later seized by the Gestapo and disappeared. In partisan circles it was generally believed he died during the last months of the conflict, in a death march.

As to the others and their subsequent doings, little or nothing is known. They have all disappeared over a period of twenty years.

THE END